ONCE UPON A SOUND

Literature-Based Phonological Activities

Linda L. Smith-Kiewel, MA, CCC-SLP
Tracy Molenaar Claeys, MS, CCC-SLP

Thinking Publications
Eau Claire, Wisconsin

11   10   09   08   07   06   05   11   10   9   8   7   6   5   4

Library of Congress Cataloging-in-Publication Data
Smith-Kiewel, Linda
    Once upon a sound : literature-based phonological activities /
Linda Smith-Kiewel, Tracy Molenaar Claeys.
       p.   cm.
    Includes bibliographical references (p.   ).
    ISBN 1-888222-31-X
    1. Articulation disorders—Treatment.   2. Speech therapy for children.   3. Language disorders in children—Treatment.   4. Speech disorders—Treatment.   5. Phonetics.   I. Claeys, Tracy Molenaar.   II. Title.
RJ496.S7S57   1998
618.92'85506—dc21   98-30856
                                               CIP

Printed in the United States of America
Illustrations by Marlene Maloney
Cover design by Kris Gausman

THINKING PUBLICATIONS
A Division of McKinley Companies, Inc.

424 Galloway Street • Eau Claire, WI 54703
715.832.2488 • Fax 715.832.9082
Email: custserv@ThinkingPublications.com
www.ThinkingPublications.com

To our families for their patience, understanding,
and support through this project

To the many children and families who helped us grow
in our clinical understanding of intervention
for children with speech and language disorders

To our colleagues, who inspired us to share

CONTENTS

PREFACE

Due to improved child identification procedures, the number of young children identified as having communication disorders has increased. Additionally, research continues to affirm the high correlation between phonological disorders and later reading, writing, and spelling problems. For these reasons, our school district asked us to explore new, effective models for serving large numbers of preschool children with highly unintelligible speech.

In 1992, we visited the preschool program in Hopkins, Minnesota and reviewed literature from the Fountain Valley Preschool Program in California. Both of these programs served children with severe phonological disorders. We also read numerous articles, attended workshops, and studied Drs. Barbara Hodson and Elaine Paden's cycles phonological remediation approach. Through many years of both clinical experience—working with young children—and personal experience—raising young children—the value of using children's literature for developing communication skills has been impressed upon us. Experience has also taught us that art, music, and play facilitate the learning of difficult objectives and that parent involvement is key to helping children use new skills in settings outside the classroom.

Given the charge to develop this preschool program, we decided to include a strong focus on children's literature; to integrate the cycles approach; to have art, music, and play be major components; to support the development of early academic skills; and to include a strong parent-involvement component. *Once Upon a Sound* is an outgrowth of this program.

After the program had been in operation for one year, Dr. Frank Cirrin, the speech-language coordinator for Minneapolis public schools, asked us to present the program to Minneapolis speech-language pathologists at a fall inservice. Presenting to over 60 colleagues was a humbling experience, but our work was well received. Many requests for us to publish followed, and we decided to embark on the task.

Our motivation to publish this resource was also influenced by our families and our Minneapolis colleagues, who continually encouraged and supported us. Now that our work is complete, we hope that your successes using this resource are many and that the activities for you and the children you serve are most enjoyable.

We wish to thank the many reviewers—Barbara Hodson, Linda Fitzgerald, Shelley Gray, Margot Kelman, Lucy Knutson, Jennifer Larsen, Julie Masterson, Angie Orth, Deborah Rubash, Mary Stapleton, and Becky Vance—for their helpful comments and suggestions in the preparation of this resource. We extend special appreciation to Dr. Frank Cirrin for his reactions to this project; to Linda Schreiber, senior editor for Thinking Publications, for her many suggestions; and to Dr. Barbara Hodson for her unparalleled contributions in the area of phonology.

INTRODUCTION

OVERVIEW

Once Upon a Sound: Literature-Based Phonological Activities is a resource to help develop the phonological skills of young children—ages three to eight years—whose speech is unintelligible. The program uses classic, familiar children's literature to help children acquire specific phonological patterns. The patterns have been selected based on Hodson and Paden's (1991) cycles phonological remediation approach. Twenty-nine lessons addressing 11 phonological patterns are provided. Each lesson uses a popular children's book to highlight the target pattern. In each lesson, target words, listening activities, production-practice activities, and art activities are based on the particular literature chosen. Because generalization of goals to other environments is so important, a letter to family members describing the lesson's goals and possible home activities also accompanies each lesson.

The importance of young children's awareness of print has always been acknowledged (Adams, 1990). *Once Upon a Sound* offers a print-rich environment that indirectly facilitates oral language development and early literacy skills in a parallel and supportive fashion. This is done, in part, through the use of books with predictable syntactical patterns, repetition, and rhyme. The books provide contextually appropriate opportunities to use language.

Phonological awareness is enhanced in the *Once Upon a Sound* lessons. As children learn to produce the phonemes, they also learn the sound-letter associations and hear words or syllables segmented. The lessons also emphasize the target phonemes through songs, rhymes, and fingerplays, as well as through a listening component in which children are auditorily bombarded with words containing the target phonemes.

Once Upon a Sound is especially useful for groups of children while implementing a cycles phonological remediation approach (Hodson and Paden, 1991). Group instruction for children with severe/profound or multiple speech disorders is effective and practical for improving speech intelligibility (Bonderman and Montgomery, 1986; Montgomery and Bonderman, 1989). However, activities in *Once Upon a Sound* are also appropriate for individualized, one-on-one phonological intervention and "traditional" articulation remediation.

SUGGESTED USERS AND SETTINGS

Once Upon a Sound is designed to help children, ages three to eight years, who are having unusual difficulty mastering an age-appropriate phonological system. However, this literature-based approach could also be used with children who have mild to moderate language delay or who show delay in developing phonological awareness and early literacy skills.

Once Upon a Sound will be useful for speech-language pathologists and other early childhood educators or Head Start teachers who teach collaboratively with speech-language pathologists. The lessons were originally written to be implemented in a phonology group setting. However, individualized instruction is also possible with slight adaptation.

FEATURES OF *ONCE UPON A SOUND*

Once Upon a Sound has many features the professional will find helpful:

1. Twenty-nine lesson plans—Each lesson focuses on a specific phonological pattern, one target phoneme or cluster, and a featured story. Procedures for implementing each lesson are provided.

2. Target word illustrations—Four 8 ½ x 5 ½" reproducible illustrations represent target words and at least one of the illustrations relates to the story in each lesson. The illustrations are used for production-practice activities and are sent home for family members to use with their child.

3. Art pages—Each lesson includes two art activities, which are geared to the interest level of young children and are designed to provide additional production-practice work. The art activities or activity pages are also sent home to family members for additional generalization opportunities.

4. An alphabetical list of books—Full publication information of the books used in the lessons is included in the bibliography (see pages 373–374).

5. A list of necessary materials—Most materials needed for the lessons are commonly found in preschool programs and/or school classrooms. They are listed as a convenience for organizing for intervention sessions (see pages 17–18).

6. Family Letters—Each lesson includes a reproducible letter for families, which describes sound formation and applicability of the selected book, presents a listening list for auditory bombardment and target words for production practice, and suggests activities for encouraging generalization. The letters also include the lyrics and words for the songs, rhymes, and fingerplays used in intervention.

7. *Ideas for Home Practice*—This reproducible handout provides ideas for helping children generalize use of the target phonemes in the home setting (see Appendix A).

8. *Remediation Data Form*—This reproducible form can be used to quantitatively measure progress in meeting intervention objectives (see Appendix B).

9. *Illustrated Alphabet*—Each letter of the alphabet (2 ½ x 2 ½") is provided for duplication in Appendix C. In most lessons, the alphabet is used to introduce the sound-letter association for the target phonemes. Although some form of the alphabet (such as magnetic alphabet or bulletin board letters) is available in most classrooms, the reproducible alphabet is provided as a convenience to educators.

SPECIFIC GOALS

Once Upon a Sound helps children meet the following goals:

1. To improve intelligibility by acquiring age-appropriate phonological patterns, including

   - Early developing patterns—syllableness, prevocalic singletons /p, m, w/, and postvocalic singletons /t, k/
   - Anterior/posterior contrasts—velars /k, g/, glottal /h/, and alveolar /t/
   - /s/ clusters—initial /st, sn, sp, sm/ and final /ps, ts/
   - Liquids—/l, r/
   - Prevocalic/postvocalic singleton strident /f/
   - Palatal sibilants—/ʃ, ʧ, ʤ/
   - Postvocalic/syllabic /r/

2. To expand oral language skills by communicating in a group about meaningful text

3. To improve phonological awareness by

   - recognizing sound-letter associations
   - understanding that words begin and end with particular sounds
   - singing songs and saying rhymes and fingerplays

4. To develop early literacy skills, including

   - using left-to-right directionality
   - understanding that print has meaning
   - distinguishing print from other graphic forms

- recognizing and singing the alphabet in sequence

- sequencing the letters in their names

BACKGROUND INFORMATION

Literature-Based Resource

Once Upon a Sound: Literature-Based Phonological Activities uses common children's literature as the basis of its lesson activities. The field of communication disorders has embraced children's literature as a viable tool for helping children with communication disorders, including those books of a phonological, morphological, syntactical, semantic, and pragmatic base. For instance, Kaderavek and Sulzby (1998) recommend parent-child joint book reading as an important component of early literacy development and as an important component in the intervention programs for some young children with language impairment. The use of storybooks that are interesting and important to children and that represent commonly occurring childhood experiences or extraordinary events is recommended by Hoffman (1992) and by Norris and Hoffman (1993). Montgomery (1992) stresses the importance of using books to reinforce literacy skills, to encourage language development, and to involve parents in the process of improving intelligibility. She highlights children's interest in books and describes the clinical benefits of using literature, such as using books to have children point out target sounds in words, to use slow and easy speech when reading, or to practice using an inside voice. In addition, Montgomery suggests using literature as a vehicle for developing communication, because as children retell the story, they are rehearsing new vocabulary; practicing different verb tenses; using complex phonology, such as *r* blends; marking sequence with concepts (e.g., then, after, finally, next); and repeating metaphors.

A benefit of using common children's books for communication development is that they are easy for family members to find. Public and school libraries are a rich source of children's books, and most parents have access to them. Family members can read the books to help children hear the target phonemes. Children can then practice producing the target phonemes when talking about the book. Books stimulate communication and encourage children's use of target phonological patterns in a new setting. In *Once Upon a Sound*, the books selected for the remediation of deviant phonological patterns are well-written and illustrated books that are familiar to and appeal to young children. The literature selections offer many opportunities for children to hear the target phonological patterns as instructors read the book and describe the illustrations.

A Phonological Remediation Approach

Once Upon a Sound is based on Hodson and Paden's (1991) cycles approach to phonological remediation, which states that children appear to acquire sounds systematically. This systematic acquisition of sounds includes both a repertoire of sounds and a complicated set of sequence patterns for language use. Children initially use simple sounds and gradually move to more complex arrangements of sounds.

Compton (1970) and Oller (1973) demonstrated that children with highly unintelligible speech have systematic ways for speaking, as do children with normally developing speech. Analysis of a child's systematic way of speaking reveals the child's phonological process patterns. Phonological patterns are considered "in error" or "deviant" when they have not developed to an age-appropriate level. A cycles phonological remediation approach to phonological disorders addresses the patterns of the child's system that are in error (Hodson, 1997, 1998; Hodson and Paden, 1991). In 1996, Klein's research supported claims that "phonological approaches to the evaluation of and intervention with children demonstrating multiple articulation disorders are more effective and efficient than the more traditional treatment procedures" (p. 321).

Cycle Programming

In Hodson and Paden's (1991) cycles phonological remediation approach, the "deficient phonological patterns are targeted in sequence and recycled (re-presented) as often as needed until the pattern emerges in conversational speech" (Hodson, 1997, p. 206). Hodson defines a cycle as "the period of time (varying in duration from 6 to 18 hours) when optimal phonological *patterns* are targeted (2 to 6 hours each)" (p. 206).

A stimulable phoneme within the deviant pattern is used to help children acquire the phonological pattern. Several phonemes can be targeted, but each is targeted for 60 minutes per cycle. Then the next stimulable pattern is targeted, using a different phoneme for 60 minutes, etc. A new cycle begins when all of the deviant patterns and phonemes that are stimulable have been addressed. This new cycle consists of addressing deviant patterns that have not yet been modified by the child. Six to eight cycles may be required before children in the profound range of unintelligibility are completely intelligible. (For more information, see the cycle examples in Appendix D).

The order for targeting the phonological patterns is determined by developmental data and by patterns that are consistently deficient and are stimulable. Figure 1 on page 7 presents a summary of patterns that might be targeted using the cycles approach.

Primary Target Patterns

As suggested in Figure 1, the primary potential target patterns for beginning cycles are early developing patterns, anterior/posterior contrasts, /s/ clusters, and liquids. Patterns are targeted only if they are consistently deficient and stimulable.

Typical beginning cycles may include early-developing patterns: syllableness and singleton consonants (if the final consonant is lacking, target voiceless stops /p/, /t/, or /k/ and/or final /m/ or /n/ if omitted). Although rare, consonant vowel (CV) productions may need to be targeted if the child is producing only vowels or vowel consonants (VC) or if a class of early-developing consonants (stops, nasals, glides) is deficient. Initial labials (e.g., /m/ and /p/) are the typical target in this instance. To address early developing patterns, *Once Upon a Sound* includes lessons for syllableness, word-initial /p, m, w/ and word-final /t, k/.

The beginning cycles may also target anterior/posterior contrasts (i.e., contrasting velars, glottals and alveolars), if they are deficient in the child's phonological system. The final /k/ should be targeted first (if deficient but stimulable), then initial /k/, /g/, and/or /h/. If there is evidence of backing (i.e., replacing an anterior consonant with a posterior one [e.g., /k/ for /t/]), the final /t/, or initial /t/ and /d/ and possibly /n/ could be targeted in beginning cycles. Anterior/posterior contrasts included in *Once Upon a Sound* lessons are word-final /k/ and word/initial /k, g, h, t/.

A typical primary target might also be /s/ clusters (word-initial /st, sn, sp, sm/ and word-final /ps, ts/). Note that the /s/ clusters are typically targeted before singleton stridents. /s/ cluster lessons included in *Once Upon a Sound* are /st, sn, sp, sm, ps, ts/.

Finally, liquids (word-initial /l/ and /r/) are also typically targeted in beginning cycles. /l/ clusters and /r/ clusters may be targeted, but the /l/ should not be targeted with labials (e.g., /fl/, /pl/, or /bl/) during beginning cycles. Lessons for liquids included in *Once Upon a Sound* are word-initial /l, r/.

Secondary Target Patterns

All primary patterns are cycled and recycled (provided they are deficient and stimulable) until they begin to emerge in conversational speech. Then secondary patterns are targeted. Secondary target patterns needing remediation usually include any patterns that remain problematic. (Note that many that were deficient during assessment may no longer be in need of remediation.) Secondary target patterns may include prevocalic voicing contrasts, vowel contrasts, singleton stridents (i.e., prevocalic /f/, /s/), palatal glide /j/, additional consonant sequences, word-medial consonants, postvocalic/syllabic /r/, assimilations, palatal sibilants

Figure 1   **Cycles Phonological Remediation Approach**

Primary Potential Target Patterns
(For beginning cycles; target only those that are consistently deficient *and* stimulable.)

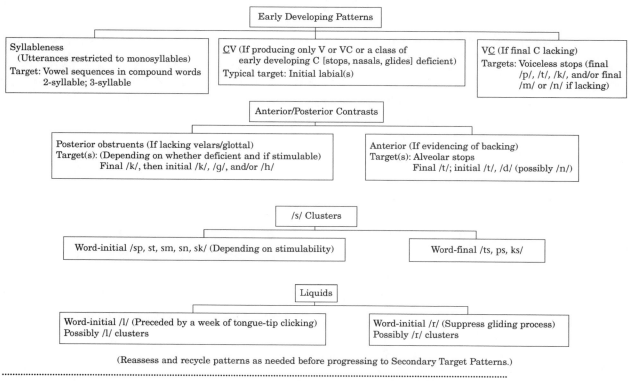

Early Developing Patterns

Syllableness
(Utterances restricted to monosyllables)
Target: Vowel sequences in compound words
2-syllable; 3-syllable

CV (If producing only V or VC or a class of
early developing C [stops, nasals, glides] deficient)
Typical target: Initial labial(s)

VC (If final C lacking)
Targets: Voiceless stops (final
/p/, /t/, /k/, and/or final
/m/ or /n/ if lacking)

Anterior/Posterior Contrasts

Posterior obstruents (If lacking velars/glottal)
Target(s): (Depending on whether deficient and if stimulable)
Final /k/, then initial /k/, /g/, and/or /h/

Anterior (If evidencing of backing)
Target(s): Alveolar stops
Final /t/; initial /t/, /d/ (possibly /n/)

/s/ Clusters

Word-initial /sp, st, sm, sn, sk/ (Depending on stimulability)

Word-final /ts, ps, ks/

Liquids

Word-initial /l/ (Preceded by a week of tongue-tip clicking)
Possibly /l/ clusters

Word-initial /r/ (Suppress gliding process)
Possibly /r/ clusters

(Reassess and recycle patterns as needed before progressing to Secondary Target Patterns.)

Secondary Potential Target Patterns
(After establishment of early developing patterns, contrastive use of velars/alveolars, /s/ cluster emergence in conversation,
and suppression of gliding while producing liquids in carefully selected production-practice words, progress to
secondary patterns that remain problematic; incorporate minimal pairs whenever possible.).

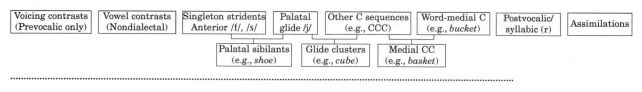

Voicing contrasts (Prevocalic only) | Vowel contrasts (Nondialectal) | Singleton stridents Anterior /f/, /s/ | Palatal glide /j/ | Other C sequences (e.g., CCC) | Word-medial C (e.g., *bucket*) | Postvocalic/ syllabic (r) | Assimilations

Palatal sibilants (e.g., *shoe*) | Glide clusters (e.g., *cube*) | Medial CC (e.g., *basket*)

Advanced Potential Target Patterns
(For upper-elementary-grade-level children with intelligibility problems)

Complex consonant sequences
(e.g., *extra*)

Multisyllabicity
(e.g., *unanimous*)

(e.g., /ʃ/), glide clusters (e.g., /kju/ in *cube*) and medial CC (e.g., /sk/ in *basket*). Note that prevocalic /f/ is a secondary target and should not be included in beginning cycles. *Once Upon a Sound* includes lessons for secondary target patterns which focus on word-initial /f, tʃ, ʃ, dʒ/, word-final /f, ʃ/, and word-final vocalic /r/.

Advanced Target Patterns

Advanced targets include complex consonant sequences (e.g., /kstr/ in *extra*) and multisyllabicity (i.e., words with three or more syllables, such as *spaghetti, macaroni,* and *aluminum*). These patterns are generally not targeted for young children and are usually reserved for school-age children with phonological disorders (Hodson, 1997). These patterns are not addressed in *Once Upon a Sound*.

Remediation Principles

Underlying principles of the cycles phonological remediation approach include emphasis on auditory, kinesthetic, and semantic awareness, a gradual increase in phonetic complexity, and the incorporation of pragmatics. *Once Upon a Sound* includes a variety of methods to help children produce specific phonological patterns. These include clinician models, placement cues, tactile cues, auditory bombardment, visual cues, mirror usage, minimal pair contrasts, breaking words apart, tongue-tip clicking, verbal directives, and, in some instances, hands-on manipulation of the articulators.

Phonological Awareness

Phonological awareness has been referred to as "the ability to reflect on and manipulate the structure of an utterance (e.g., into words, syllables, or sounds) as distinct from meaning" (Stackhouse, 1997, p. 197). Children with little awareness of the phonological elements of language tend to be at risk for reading, writing, and spelling difficulties (Bird, Bishop, and Freeman, 1995; Blachman, 1984; Bradley and Bryant, 1983; Catts, 1993; Clarke-Klein, 1994; Gierut, 1998; Hodson and Edwards, 1997; Hoffman, 1992). The value of phonological awareness enhancing activities to help reduce these risks has been described by Catts (1991), Kamhi (1992), and Hodson (1998).

Anderson and Graham (1994) and van Kleeck (1993) recommend the use of music, nursery rhymes, poems, and rhythmic games to "help establish rhythmic speech and phonological awareness" (p. 96). Adams (1990) also describes the importance of using music to develop phonological awareness, using as an example, how the familiar melody of "Twinkle, Twinkle, Little Star" helps children learn the alphabet when singing the "Alphabet Song." McFadden (1998) advocates teaching phonological awareness within meaningful textual experiences.

In *Once Upon a Sound*, focusing on pattern use by targeting only one phoneme encourages development of phonological awareness. For example, each phoneme is associated with a letter or letter combination; a motoric movement; a character or object from a book; and one or more songs, rhymes, or fingerplays. This is an important part of the program because research has shown the importance of providing phonological awareness activities along with phonology intervention (Clarke-Klein, 1994; Hodson, 1994; Jenkins and Bowen, 1994; Stone, 1992). Children with expressive phonological disorders have difficulty developing phonological awareness (Stackhouse, 1992). As mentioned earlier, children with phonological awareness difficulties are further at risk for reading, writing, and spelling problems.

For these reasons, *Once Upon a Sound* provides opportunities for singing, rhyming, saying fingerplays, blending sounds, segmenting sounds, and making sound-letter associations. Many of the books contain repetitive lines that remain constant throughout the story (e.g., in the story *Jump, Frog, Jump!* [Kalan, 1995], the line "Jump, frog, jump!" is repeated throughout). This repetition helps the child use longer phrases with increased linguistic and phonological complexity and provides awareness of phonological elements necessary for literacy success.

Other Communication Goals

Voice

While the primary purpose of *Once Upon a Sound* is to remediate children's phonology, literature-based instruction allows creative clinicians to facilitate other communication goals, such as reduction of vocal abuse. In addition to the opportunity for providing appropriate models and an environment with reduced background noise, instances of vocal abuse/misuse can be identified and discussed with the child. Alternate vocal and/or gestural behaviors can be taught and modeled for the child. Vocal behavior can be monitored, and instances of abuse can be documented and brought to the child's attention. Self-awareness and encouragement for the child to modify his or her vocal use can also be promoted.

Fluency

Excessive disfluencies and disordered phonology often co-occur in young children (Kelman and Edwards, 1994). Johnson and Heinze (1994) recommend to begin with fluency therapy and then to "gradually work into a combined fluency and phonology program" (p. 66). Lessons in *Once Upon a Sound* can be used to promote fluent speech by including the use of a slow speaking rate by the clinician and the use of extensive modeling of fluent productions. Indirect reinforcement and modeling of slow, easy speech can be provided in appropriate and natural ways.

Syntax, Semantics, and Pragmatics

Many children with severe phonological disorders also do poorly on language tests measuring syntax and vocabulary (Ruscello, 1991). This is a concern because children with language learning disorders are at risk for academic and learning problems (Cirrin, 1994). Intervention for some phonological processes, such as final consonant deletion, has the potential to improve the acquisition of verb tenses, contractions, plurals, possessives, and comparatives. *Once Upon a Sound* also offers children opportunities to use language functionally and meaningfully for a variety of communication purposes while addressing the specific phonological process deviations within a child's phonological system. The use of books and the ensuing discussions serve to develop children's vocabulary knowledge and to improve their pragmatic language skills.

HOW TO USE *ONCE UPON A SOUND*

Determining Needs

Before beginning to use *Once Upon a Sound*, the child's communication skills should be evaluated. Children with severe intelligibility problems should have a complete phonological analysis. The patterns to be targeted and the direction for remediation are then determined from the phonological analysis.

Phonological patterns can be examined by single words (Hodson, 1986; Khan and Lewis, 1986), and by conversation (Grunwell, 1985; Shriberg and Kwiatkowski, 1980). *The Assessment of Phonological Processes-Revised (APP-R)* (Hodson, 1986) is one method for evaluating phonological deviations in a child's speech. This assessment requires transcriptions of single words from conversation. Percentages of inaccurate phonological patterns and a severity interval can be computed, thereby identifying phonological deviations needing remediation. *Computer Analysis of Phonological Processes* (Hodson, 1985) and *Computer Analysis of Phonological Deviations* (Hodson, 1992) are software programs that analyze single-word transcriptions from the *APP-R* and then compute the percentages and patterns needing remediation. The programs are timesavers and greatly expedite the assessment process. Using the *APP-R* analysis or another assessment device, educators can target patterns from percentage-of-occurrence scores that exceed 40 percent for remediation. Target phonemes to remediate specific deviant phonological patterns are then identified using the child's transcription recording and measures of stimulability.

After determining the patterns to remediate, the lessons can be selected. For example, if you determine that intervention should begin with remediation of postvocalic consonant deletion using word-final /t/ as the target phoneme, the *I Went Walking* lesson could be chosen.

Amount of Time and Frequency of Instruction

The amount of time and frequency of intervention should be based on each child's needs. Intervention in small groups (from three to six children) for one-hour sessions at least two times each week appears to be effective when provided to preschool children who have severe phonological disorders (Smith-Kiewel and Claeys, 1997). Children in the profound range of phonological deviancy appear to profit from four one-hour sessions weekly (Smith-Kiewel, and Claeys, 1997). The same phonological pattern and target words might be used for all four sessions. However, four sessions may not be necessary if effective home stimulation is provided. See Appendix E for specific service/outcome data achieved using *Once Upon a Sound* at the Minneapolis public schools' Early Childhood Special Education (ECSE) speech and language program at St. Helena School.

Each phonological pattern should be facilitated for approximately two hours. A new phonological pattern or different phonemes within the same pattern may then be introduced. (A shorter amount of time may be needed for sessions with individual children.) Phonological patterns needing remediation are presented in succession until all have been presented. This could take from 5 to 20 weeks, depending on how often the children are seen for intervention. When all phonological patterns, which are deficient but stimulable, have been presented, one cycle is complete. Patterns are then recycled until the patterns begin to emerge in the child's spontaneous speech (most patterns are recycled two or more times). In *Once Upon a Sound*, phonemes/patterns typically needing recycling are presented in two lessons. A second lesson is provided for word-initial /k, l, f/.

When using *Once Upon a Sound* in a group setting, the same target phonological pattern could be the focus for all children in the group, even though the pattern may not be an area of need for each child. Children not needing remediation of a particular pattern are excellent models and profit from the success they enjoy. With creativity, the literature, suggested activities, and art pages can provide many opportunities for generalization of previously learned phonological patterns (e.g., you can use a carrier phrase or sentence that incorporates another child's target).

Using the Lessons in *Once Upon a Sound*

As described in "Background Information," *Once Upon a Sound* lessons are literature based; include developmentally appropriate art, music, and play activities; have a strong family component; and encourage phonological awareness and literacy development. Each lesson focuses on a particular book. Each lesson also includes illustrated target words, a listening list, art pages, and a Family Letter which are used to focus on a particular deviant phonological pattern. Generally, one lesson is taught per week. The next week, a new lesson with either a different phoneme or cluster from the same phonological pattern or a different phoneme or cluster from a different phonological pattern is used.

Once Upon a Sound was written as a phonology group intervention resource. Each lesson describes activities at four main centers: (1) an opening center, (2) a listening center, (3) a practice center, and (4) an art center. The following sections describe each center. If using this resource for a phonology group in a classroom setting, organize the classroom into these four centers. (Although written with groups in mind, speech-language pathologists can easily adapt *Once Upon a Sound* to provide individualized instruction to children. The room arrangement would not be "center oriented," although all activities described in the lessons could be implemented.)

Opening Center

The opening center is where children initially gather for greetings and an introduction to the lessons. The goal of the opening center is to introduce the target phonemes that facilitate specific phonological patterns.

The sessions should usually begin with some free conversation time, a review of the previous session's target words (if appropriate), and probing (i.e., determining which, if any, new targets are emerging). During this time, emerging phonological patterns can be noted. A short opening song may also be sung to establish group behavior and child interest.

The target phonemes are introduced using a set of alphabet letters to emphasize the sound-letter correspondence (if appropriate). Appendix C includes a set of alphabet letters to use during the opening center, but a set of magnetized alphabet letters and a magnetic board may also be used. If using the alphabet in Appendix C, duplicate the *Illustrated Alphabet* onto card stock, color, and laminate if desired. Then cut apart the cards. Display them in the classroom to use while introducing the letters/phonemes and while singing the "Alphabet Song." As an option, have an extra alphabet set available so that you can hold up the target letters when introducing them. Note that some lessons target consonant blends (e.g., *sk*) and diagraphs (e.g., *sh*). Demonstrating sound-letter correspondence in these lessons may be confusing to young children so it should be done at your discretion. Also note that in some lessons a target word may begin with the target phoneme but may not be spelled with the expected letter (e.g., *one* for /w/, *phone* for /f/).

In the opening center, children learn the names and sounds of the letters. The letters are identified within the order of the letters in the alphabet. Each child is asked to produce the target phoneme(s) in isolation. Assistance may be needed to elicit the target phonemes. Many lessons in *Once Upon a Sound* include Helpful

Hints (placed as a sidebar) which describe a variety of methods to help facilitate target phoneme productions. Helpful Hints include visual models, tactile or kinesthetic cues, or segmentation suggestions.

During the opening center, focus books are introduced and then read. The target phonemes are identified when they occur in words in the stories. Songs, rhymes, and fingerplays containing the target phonemes are practiced. Each lesson includes two examples for use.

Optional activities, which promote phonological awareness and provide auditory bombardment, may also be a part of the opening center. Optional activities are presented as sidebars in the lessons. The activities suggest placing objects containing the target phonemes in a bucket. As children do activities such as grab objects from the bucket, the objects are named for the children to listen to or imitate.

Listening Center

The goal of the listening center is to provide clear auditory stimuli of the targeted patterns and phonemes. At the listening center, children sit at a table with headphones connected to an amplifier held by the speech-language pathologist. Children listen with slight amplification as a list of words containing the target phonemes is read. Amplification can be achieved by having the children wear headsets while the speech-language pathologist speaks into a microphone. A small amplifier, headsets, and connectors can be purchased at any electronic supply store (e.g., Radio Shack). If amplification equipment is not available, the listening list can still be read to the children. In this case, ask the children to listen carefully as you clearly articulate the words on the listening list. A listening list is included in each lesson. Words from the books that are familiar to children and that are related to common experiences were selected to develop the lists. The words are to be read to the children to auditorily bombard them with the target pattern (Hodson, 1997).

Before the session, one set of target word illustrations are duplicated for clinician use. Then, in the listening center, the four target words are introduced and modeled using the target word illustrations duplicated for the clinician. To encourage self-monitoring, children take turns saying and listening to their own productions of the target words while wearing their headsets. Adaptations should be made to individualize productions based on each child's level.

Play dough activities are used at the listening center to maintain the children's attention and to provide a medium for additional target phoneme practice. Concepts can also be enhanced using play dough with the optional target-related manipulatives (e.g., big and little star cookie cutters could be used to facilitate the /st/ blend and the concepts big and little).

Practice Center

After the children have finished work at the listening center, they move to the practice center. The goal of the practice center is to achieve correct production of the phonological pattern in the target words using the target word illustrations. Each phonological pattern is remediated using four specific, carefully selected target words. Facilitating contexts (i.e., phonetic environments which may be likely to facilitate correct production of a phoneme [Kent, 1982]) were considered when selecting the target words. In addition, when choosing the target words, at least one word connected with the focus book was chosen.

At the practice center, the children sit at a small table to practice the lessons' target words while they color the target word illustrations. To prepare for the practice center, create one name card per child using construction paper. (The name card can be reused in each lesson.) Place the name cards around the table. Each child eventually learns to recognize his or her printed name. Once the children identify their names, help them finger-trace the letters of their names by placing your hand over the child's hand and tracing together. While each letter is traced, say the name of the letter and then have the child imitate your model. If their names include the target phonemes, point them out. Letter identification, letter naming, phoneme production, and sound sequencing are enhanced with this activity.

Work at the practice center continues with the children engaging in production-practice activities. While practicing the four target words with an individual child, you may need to facilitate production of the target phoneme(s) by using a variety of methods, including use of visual, auditory, and tactile cues; segmentation of words; and placement cues. The other children in the group can color the target word illustrations while each child is worked with individually, but be aware that peer modeling is an important occurrence at the practice center.

While it is extremely helpful if the phonemes are stimulable in the target words, success is not dependent on immediate stimulability. Experience has shown that mastery is often achieved in later cycles by facilitation for specific phonological patterns in earlier cycles. For example, during an early cycle, a postvocalic /k/ might be achieved only when the speech-language pathologist uses a tongue depressor to apply slight pressure on the tongue tip. In a later cycle, this child may spontaneously produce postvocalic /k/ in words.

Sometimes correct phoneme production is achieved only when words are segmented or broken apart; other times correct phoneme production is achieved only when phonemes are in isolation; and still other times only features of the phoneme are achieved. Even though facilitating contexts were considered when choosing target words, such contexts may not be ideal for a specific child. Specific adaptations may be needed to accommodate different children's capabilities.

Therefore, 100 percent accuracy in producing the target phoneme(s) in a word may not always be possible, but a close approximation will facilitate the gradual acquisition of the specific pattern and phoneme(s). Kaufman (1997) recommends that the educator model *word shells* if children do not have complete articulatory accuracy at the word level (e.g., the educator models *apple* by saying [æpo]). The word shells—which provide a lesser degree of articulatory accuracy at this level—are then imitated by the child. Experience indicates that acceptable productions made by children in the profound range of phonological severity may need to be close approximations or word shells.

The value of the cycles approach is that one week the phonological pattern may be quite easy for the child to master, while the next week's pattern may be quite challenging. The cycles approach allows for gradual acquisition of age-appropriate phonological patterns.

During the practice center, keep a log of each child's progress. Data regarding the child's mastery of the target phonemes can be recorded on the *Remediation Data Form,* provided in Appendix B (see an explanation for using the form on page 18). The child's production of the target phoneme(s) in the target words is considered an accurate response. If the child produces the target phoneme(s) only following your model, the child's response would be considered an inaccurate production, but one that is closer to being acquired. What the child does produce could be recorded on the *Remediation Data Form.*

Notes can be written to parents on each child's Family Letter, or on the target word illustrations, regarding any special considerations pertaining to the child's level of performance. Tangible reinforcement (e.g., stickers) can be provided at the end of the child's production-practice time. Stickers of objects whose names contain the target phonemes are particularly motivating. Sticker ideas are provided in each lesson. Stickers can be applied to a speech folder created for each child (see pages 16–17).

Art Center

At the art center, children complete the two art activities included in each lesson. The goal of the art center is to provide additional modeling of the target phonemes and to provide additional production practice. The art activities also are good visual aids for family members to use in home activities.

Each lesson includes two or three art pages that provide opportunities for generalizing the target phoneme(s). Spontaneous, interactive conversation with peers can be elicited through the art. This allows you to listen for emerging phonological patterns. In most lessons, one of the art pages also relates to the focus book.

In this way, the intervention session is meaningful, familiar, and highly interesting to the children. Instructions on the art pages describe what the children are to do.

The art pages (or product, such as a stick puppet) are placed in the children's speech folders and then sent home with them. Children are proud of these pages, so they are powerful motivators for using the target phonemes at home.

Each lesson also includes ideas for a snack to be brought out at the end of the session, usually following the practice center. The suggested snacks include the target phonemes (e.g., chocolate chip cookies for word-initial /tʃ/) and can be used to elicit the target phonemes. Elicitations should be based on each child's skill level.

Home Practice

There are several ways families are involved in *Once Upon a Sound*. One family component is the handout *Ideas for Home Practice* (see Appendix A). This handout can be given to family members to help them understand their child's intervention program. *Ideas for Home Practice* encourages families to help their child generalize skills to the home setting. If opportunities are provided in the home setting, progress toward meeting remediation goals is greatly enhanced (Broen, Doyle, and Bacon, 1993; Shelton, Johnson, and Arndt, 1972).

Each lesson in *Once Upon a Sound* also includes a Family Letter, which can be sent home with the child when beginning a new lesson. The letter describes the lesson's objectives and any special considerations (i.e., individualized adaptations) that may need to be provided. It also describes how to produce the target phoneme(s), lists the target words, and describes the focus book. Suggestions for home practice activities are also provided in the Family Letter.

Additionally, a speech folder containing target word illustrations and artwork can be sent back and forth between school and home. The speech folder is an ideal way to keep communication two-way.

Preparing for the Lessons

Creating a Speech Folder

Although optional, it is helpful for each child to have his or her own speech folder. A speech folder can be created from a folder with two pockets. Target word illustrations, art pages, Family Letters, and special correspondence can go back and forth with the child in the folder after each intervention session.

After the child has practiced the target words, the child can place tangible reinforcers (e.g., stickers) on the outside of the folder. Seeing the collection of stickers earned over time is usually quite motivating for children. The speech folder becomes very important to each child because of the successes and accomplishments it represents.

Gathering Materials

Before using the lessons in *Once Upon a Sound*, also do the following:

1. Prepare a name card (see page 14) and *Remediation Data Form* for each child.

2. Gather the amplification equipment (amplifier, headsets, and connectors) suggested for the listening center, if available.

3. Duplicate for each child the lessons' target word illustrations, art pages, and Family Letter.

4. Gather the set of alphabet letters, focus book, play dough, and art materials.

5. Refer to the chosen lesson plan to determine other art materials needed.

The following materials are often used within the *Once Upon a Sound* lessons and are listed here as a convenience for organizing for intervention sessions.

1-inch blocks
8 ½ by 11" paper (white and blue)
aluminum foil
bucket or container
cereal (e.g., Cocoa Puffs, Peanut Butter Puffs, Alpha-Bits)
chalk (colored and white)
colored markers
colored pencils
construction paper (various colors and sizes)
cookie cutters (e.g., dog, peach, pear, pig, alphabet letters)
corn syrup
cotton balls (colored and white)
cotton swabs (e.g., Q-tips)
crackers (e.g., Teddy Grahams)
crayons
facial tissues (e.g., Kleenex)
feathers
finger paint
food coloring
glitter (colored and white)
glitter crayons

glitter glue
glitter pens
glue (colored and white)
marshmallows (miniature)
mirror
one set of alphabet letters (Appendix C) or
   a set of magnetized alphabet letters and a magnetic board
paintbrushes
paper punch
paste
plastic bowls, plates, utensils (e.g., knives, forks, spoons)
play dough
popped popcorn
popsicle sticks
rubber stamps
salt
scissors
shredded coconut
soft crayons (e.g., Craypas)
sponges
stapler and staples
stickers
straws
tea
tempera paint
tissue paper (yellow)
tongue depressors
two-pocket folders
watercolor paints
yarn

Using the Remediation Data Form

Results of the practice session can be recorded on a *Remediation Data Form*. A blank *Remediation Data Form* is provided in Appendix B. Performance data can be recorded, as well as specific notes and observations. To use the form, record the date, the target pattern or phoneme(s), the lesson used, and the child's performance at spontaneously producing the target words during the practice center time. Additional notes and observations can also be recorded since they will be helpful for program planning. Figure 2 presents an example of a completed *Remediation Data Form*.

Figure 2   **Example Remediation Data Form**

Name: _Jessie_

Speech-Language Pathologist: _Tracy Smith_

DATE	TARGET	LESSON	RESULTS
Sept. 14–18	Syllableness	Brown Bear, Brown Bear, What Do You See? • black sheep • blue horse • red bird • white dog	Day 1—Target: 2/4 Day 2—Target: 4/4 Observation: age-appropriate use of syllableness omits most final consonants
Sept. 21–25	Word-initial /w/	Wheels on the Bus • window • wiper • one • walk	Day 1—Target: 2/4 Day 2—Target: 4/4 Observation: • good lip rounding • word-initial /w/ generalized
Sept. 28–Oct. 2	Word-initial /m/	Goodnight Moon • moon • mush • mouse • mitten	Day 1—Target: 2/4 Day 2—Target: 4/4 Observation: word-initial /m/ seems to have generalized
Oct. 5–9	Word-initial /p/	Each Peach Pear Plum • pop • pie • pig • peach	Day 1—Target: 2/4 Day 2—Target: 3/4 Observation: inconsistently voicing p → b and/or using nasality p → m
Oct. 12–16	Word-final /t/	I Went Walking • hat • night • wet • toot	Day 1—Target: 0/4 Day 2—Target: 2/4 Observation: continues to omit final consonant inconsistently; stimulable at the VC level
Oct. 19–23	Word-final /k/	Shake My Sillies Out • knock • walk • back • hook	Day 1—Target: 2/4 Day 2—Target: 3/4 Observation: beginning to generalize final consonant use

PRIMARY
TARGET PATTERNS:
EARLY DEVELOPING
PATTERNS

BROWN BEAR, BROWN BEAR, WHAT DO YOU SEE?

PATTERN

Syllableness

TARGET

Two-syllable productions

TARGET WORDS

red bird, black sheep, white dog, blue horse

OPENING CENTER

GOAL

To introduce syllableness

MATERIAL

1. Book titled *Brown Bear, Brown Bear, What Do You See?* (1983), by Bill Martin Jr.

PROCEDURE

1. Introduce *Brown Bear, Brown Bear, What Do You See?* Have the children take turns finger-tracing the title to introduce left-to-right orientation.

2. Read *Brown Bear, Brown Bear, What Do You See?* As you read the story to the children, instruct them to repeat the names of the animals after you. The goal is to imitate the correct number of syllables in words and word combinations.

> **Optional Materials**
>
> *Bucket of objects such as a hot dog, an apple, a banana or "nana," a cookie, a cowboy, a mailbox, a train to elicit "choo choo"*

Helpful Hint

When attempting correct syllable production, it is often beneficial to pair a motoric movement (e.g., tapping, slapping, clapping) with a verbal production. This pairing of motor movement with verbal movement often facilitates correct syllable production. It is also very motivating for the children.

Optional Activity

Have the children close their eyes and reach into the bucket for an object. Model the name of the object, articulating the two-syllable productions. Have the children produce the words or word approximation after your model.

3. Say the fingerplay "Open Shut Them" and sing the song "_____'s Wearing Brown Shoes."

"Open Shut Them"
(Gesture with your hands. Have the children try to imitate the gestures.)

Open shut them, open shut them,
give a little clap.

Open shut them, open shut them,
put them in your lap.

Creep them, creep them, creep them, creep them,
right up to your chin.

Open wide your little mouth, but do not let them in.

"_____'s Wearing Brown Shoes"
(Fill in the blanks with children's names and appropriate shoe colors.)

_____'s wearing brown shoes, brown shoes,
brown shoes.
_____'s wearing brown shoes all day long.

LISTENING CENTER

GOAL

To provide clear auditory stimuli for syllableness

MATERIALS

1. One amplifier and one connector with headset per child

2. Listening list: *brown bear, red bird, blue horse, green frog, white dog, black sheep, goldfish, yellow duck, purple cat*

3. Illustrations of the four target words (pages 28–29; duplicate, cut out, and staple together)

4. Play dough

PROCEDURE

1. Instruct the children to wear their headsets and to listen. Speak into the amplifier and read the listening list to the children.

2. Introduce the target words—*red bird, black sheep, white dog, blue horse*—to the children using the illustrations.

3. Instruct the children to continue wearing their headsets as you present a model of each target word. Have the children take turns repeating each word after it has been presented to each of them.

4. Give the play dough to the children. Demonstrate to the children how they can squeeze, roll, pat, and/or push the play dough while they listen to the productions in their headsets.

PRACTICE CENTER

GOAL

To facilitate production of syllableness

MATERIALS

1. One printed name card per child (see page 14)

2. Illustrations of the four target words (pages 28–29; duplicate, cut out, and staple together one set per child)

3. Colored markers

4. Each child's *Remediation Data Form* (Appendix B)

5. *Family Letter* (pages 33–34; duplicate one per child)

6. One speech folder per child

Optional Materials
Stickers that will facilitate two-syllable productions (e.g., brown bear, hot dog, or baseball stickers)

PROCEDURE

1. Have the children find their own name card. Once identified, instruct the children to finger-trace and say the letters in their names.

2. Instruct the children to color the four target word illustrations—*red bird, black sheep, white dog, blue horse*—using the colored markers.

3. Have the children take turns naming the target word illustrations. The goal is to elicit the child's spontaneous productions of two syllables or more.

4. Document the children's productions on their *Remediation Data Form*.

5. Write notes related to each child's goal on his or her *Family Letter*.

Optional Activity
Have the children choose a sticker to put on their folders. Elicit two-syllable productions from each child by asking them to name the sticker.

ART CENTER

GOAL

To provide additional syllableness production practice and to create visual aids for home activities

MATERIALS

1. *Brown Bear* (page 30; duplicate one per child)

2. Brown watercolor paint

3. One paintbrush per child

4. *Animal Puppets* (pages 31–32; duplicate one per child)

5. One set of crayons per child (brown, red, yellow, green, purple, white, blue, black, orange [for goldfish])

6. Scissors

7. Stapler

8. One set of nine popsicle sticks per child

PROCEDURE

Brown Bear

1. Using the brown watercolor paints, have the children paint the bear brown. Ask the children to imitate the words *brown bear* as they paint. The children can also imitate other models you provide (e.g., brown ear, brown eye, brown nose, etc.)

2. Allow the art page to dry, and then send it home in the child's speech folder the following session.

Animal Puppets

1. Have the children use the appropriate crayons to color the animals (e.g., color the bear brown and the duck yellow).

2. Cut out each animal including its corresponding label.

3. Staple each animal onto a popsicle stick. Give each child a set of nine animal puppets.

4. Have the children hold up the animal puppet and name (or imitate) the animal and its color.

5. Send the animal puppets home in the child's speech folder.

HOME PRACTICE

GOAL

To provide home suggestions for what the children can do in the context of their everyday lives

MATERIALS

1. Each child's set of colored target word illustrations

2. Each child's completed art page and animal puppets

3. Each child's speech folder

4. Each child's *Family Letter*

PROCEDURE

1. Collect the children's colored target word illustrations, completed art page, and animal puppets, and send them home in their speech folders.

2. Write any special instructions specific to a child on the *Family Letter*, on the target word illustrations, or on the art pages.

> **Optional Snack Activity**
>
> *At the end of the session, set out a snack that will facilitate syllable production (e.g., a cookie, an apple, a banana, etc.). Have each child request a snack using a production based on his or her skill level.*

red bird

black sheep

white dog

blue horse

Paint the bear brown.
Say "brown bear, brown bear"
while you paint.

goldfish

yellow duck

black sheep

purple cat

Color the animal puppets.
Say the name of each puppet
when you color it.

Animal Puppets

brown bear

red bird

blue horse

green frog

white dog

Family Letter

Date: _____

Dear Family,

This lesson focuses on producing the correct number of syllables when speaking. The goal is to correctly produce two or three syllable words or phrases (e.g., brown bear, purple cat). Some children might be asked to produce the correct number of syllables in complex sentences (e.g., "I see a red bird looking at me").

We have chosen the book *Brown Bear, Brown Bear, What Do You See?* by Bill Martin Jr. and Eric Carle for this lesson. This story has lots of opportunities for children to hear and use the correct number of syllables.

Listening List

Read this list to your child. The goal is to model two syllables.

brown bear	red bird
blue horse	green frog
white dog	black sheep
goldfish	teacher

Target Words

Using the pages in the speech folder, practice these four sets of words with your child. The goal is to produce two syllables, not necessarily to name the correct color.

blue horse	red bird
black sheep	white dog

Suggested Home Activities

1. Read the story *Brown Bear, Brown Bear, What Do You See?* Slow your rate of speaking for the target words *red bird, black sheep, white dog,* and *blue horse.* Have your child listen carefully to the syllables.

2. Play with toy animals and a farm set. Model and practice the target pattern of syllableness (e.g., *brown horse, black pig, orange cat*).

3. Have your child say the color and names of their clothing (e.g., *white shirt, blue coat, red cap*).

4. Have your child say goodnight to animals and objects in the bedroom (e.g., "Night, Bear").

5. Play games with the animal puppets your child brings home in his or her speech folder. For example, hold all the animal puppets and have your child

pick one puppet at a time. Each time your child selects a puppet, have your child name the animal puppet using the correct number of syllables.

6. Review the *Brown Bear* art your child brings home. Practice saying various parts of the bear (e.g., *brown eye, brown ear*). Remember that the goal is to use the correct number of syllables, not necessarily to say each sound correctly.

Fingerplays and Songs

The following fingerplay and song are being practiced in class. You can help your child use syllableness by having him or her listen as you slightly emphasize the underlined words and slightly slow your rate of speaking.

"<u>Open</u> Shut Them"
(Gesture this fingerplay with your hands. Have your child try to imitate the gestures.)

<u>Open</u> shut them, <u>open</u> shut them,
give a <u>little</u> clap.

<u>Open</u> shut them, <u>open</u> shut them,
put them in your lap.

Creep them, creep them, creep them, creep them,
right up to your chin.

<u>Open</u> wide your <u>little</u> mouth, but do not let them in.

"_____'s <u>Wearing</u> <u>Brown</u> <u>Shoes</u>"
(Fill in the blanks with children's names and appropriate shoe colors.)

_____'s <u>wearing</u> <u>brown shoes</u>, <u>brown shoes</u>,
brown shoes.
_____'s <u>wearing</u> <u>brown shoes</u> all day long.

Special Considerations

Sincerely,

_____

EACH PEACH PEAR PLUM

PATTERN

Prevocalic singleton

TARGET PHONEME

Word-initial /p/

TARGET WORDS

pie, peach, pop, pig

OPENING CENTER

GOAL

To introduce word-initial /p/

MATERIALS

1. One set of alphabet letters (Appendix C)

2. Facial tissue

3. Book titled *Each Peach Pear Plum* (1978), by Janet and Allan Ahlberg

> **Optional Materials**
>
> *Bucket of objects such as a peach, a pear, popcorn, pop, a pickle, a pen, a puppy, a pig*

PROCEDURE

1. Introduce the letter *p* in the set of alphabet letters and demonstrate correct production of /p/. Hold the facial tissue in front of your mouth and instruct the children to watch the facial tissue move as the air for /p/ makes an explosive sound. Sing the "Alphabet Song" (to the tune of "Twinkle, Twinkle, Little Star") and point to the letter *p* in the set of alphabet letters.

2. Have the children produce /p/ while you hold the tissue in front of their mouths. Children enjoy seeing the tissue move.

3. Introduce *Each Peach Pear Plum*. Point out the letter *p* in the title words *peach, pear,* and *plum*. Have the children take turns finger-tracing the letter *p* as you articulate /p/ in the title words *peach, pear,* and *plum*.

4. Read *Each Peach Pear Plum*. Model word-initial /p/ in the words *peach, pear,* and *pie*.

5. Sing the song "Pop Goes the Weasel" and say the fingerplay "Pat-a-Cake." Model /p/ when it occurs in the word-initial position. (For extra enjoyment, use a jack-in-the-box toy for the *pop* of "Pop Goes the Weasel.")

"Pop Goes the Weasel"

All around the mulberry bush.
The monkey chased the weasel.
The monkey thought it was all in fun.
Pop goes the weasel!

"Pat-a-Cake"

Pat-a-cake, pat-a-cake, baker's man,
Bake me a cake as fast as you can;
Pat it and pat it, and mark it with P,
Put it in the oven for Baby and me.

LISTENING CENTER

GOAL

To provide clear auditory stimuli for word-initial /p/

MATERIALS

1. One amplifier and one connector with headset per child

2. Listening list: *pea, pep, peep, pup, pickle, pear, plum, pen, pipe, pan*

3. Illustrations of the four target words (pages 40–41; duplicate, cut out, and staple together)

4. Play dough

5. Tiny, shallow bowl or plate

6. One popsicle stick per child

PROCEDURE

1. Instruct the children to wear their headsets and to listen. Speak into the amplifier and read the listening list to the children.

2. Introduce the four target words—*pie, peach, pop, pig*—to the children using the illustrations.

3. Instruct the children to continue wearing their headsets as you present a model of each target word. Have the children take turns repeating each word after it has been presented to each of them.

4. Help the children make peas from the play dough. Elicit the word *pea* from each child. Use the tiny, shallow bowl or plate to make a play dough "pie." Elicit the word *pie* from each child. Help the children make a long oval ball. Put a popsicle stick lengthwise through the middle of each ball. Tell the children they have made a "popsicle." Elicit the word *pop* from each child.

Optional Activity

Using the play dough and the cookie cutters, help the children cut out pears, peaches, pigs, or the letter p. *Elicit* /p/.

PRACTICE CENTER

GOAL

To facilitate production of word-initial /p/

MATERIALS

1. One printed name card per child (see page 14)

2. Illustrations of the four target words (pages 40–41; duplicate, cut out, and staple together one set per child)

3. Colored markers

4. Each child's *Remediation Data Form* (Appendix B)

5. *Family Letter* (pages 44–45; duplicate one per child)

6. One speech folder per child

Optional Materials

Stickers beginning with /p/ *(e.g., popsicle, puppy, or pig stickers)*

PROCEDURE

1. Have the children find their own name card. Once identified, instruct the children to finger-trace and say the letters in their names.

2. Instruct the children to color the four target word illustrations—*pie, peach, pop, pig*—using the colored markers.

3. Have the children take turns naming the target word illustrations. The goal is to elicit word-initial /p/.

4. Document the children's productions on their *Remediation Data Form*.

5. Write notes related to each child's goal on his or her *Family Letter*.

ART CENTER

GOAL

To provide additional word-initial /p/ production practice and to create visual aids for home activities

MATERIALS

1. *Peach and Pear* (page 42; duplicate one per child)

2. Food coloring (orange and yellow)

3. Corn syrup or white glue

4. Two small paper cups

5. Two cotton swabs per child

6. *Popcorn* (page 43; duplicate one per child)

7. Popped popcorn

8. Paste

PROCEDURE

Peach and Pear

1. Mix food coloring with either corn syrup or white glue (orange food coloring for the peach and yellow food coloring for the pear).

2. Put the mixtures in two separate paper cups with a cotton swab for each child in each cup.

3. Have the children use the cotton swabs to paint the peach with the orange mixture and the pear with the yellow mixture. (A corn syrup mixture creates a glossy finish but takes longer to dry than a glue mixture.)

4. Elicit word-initial /p/ for both of the fruits (i.e., *peach* and *pear*) as the children paint.

5. Allow the art page to dry, and then send it home in the child's speech folder the following session.

Popcorn

1. Have the children use paste to paste popcorn in the bowl on the art page.

2. Elicit the word *pop* from each child several times.

3. Allow the art page to dry, and then send it home in the child's speech folder the following session.

HOME PRACTICE

GOAL

To provide home suggestions for what the children can do in the context of their everyday lives

MATERIALS

1. Each child's set of colored target word illustrations

2. Each child's completed art pages

3. Each child's speech folder

4. Each child's *Family Letter*

PROCEDURE

1. Collect the children's colored target word illustrations and completed art pages, and send them home in their speech folders.

2. Write any special instructions specific to a child on the *Family Letter*, on the target word illustrations, or on the art pages.

> **Optional Snack Activity**
>
> *At the end of the session, set out a snack beginning with /p/ (e.g., popsicles, pieces of a peach or pear, or popcorn). Have each child request a snack using a production based on his or her skill level.*

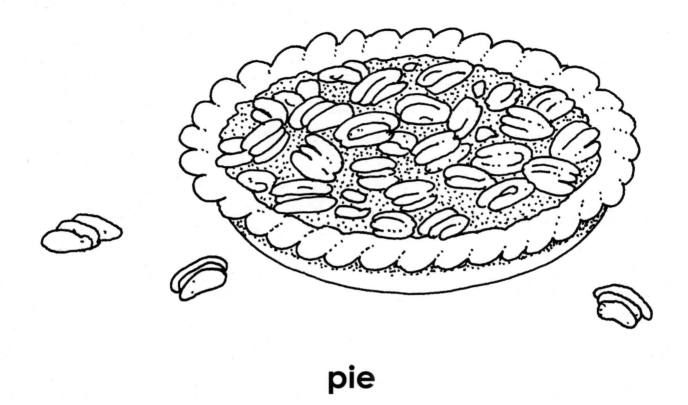

pie

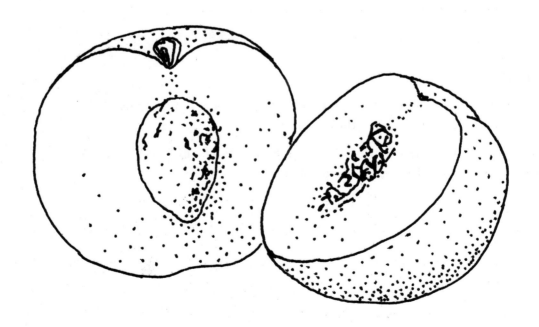

peach

pop

pig

Peach and Pear

Paint the peach and the pear.
Talk about the painted peach and pear.

Popcorn

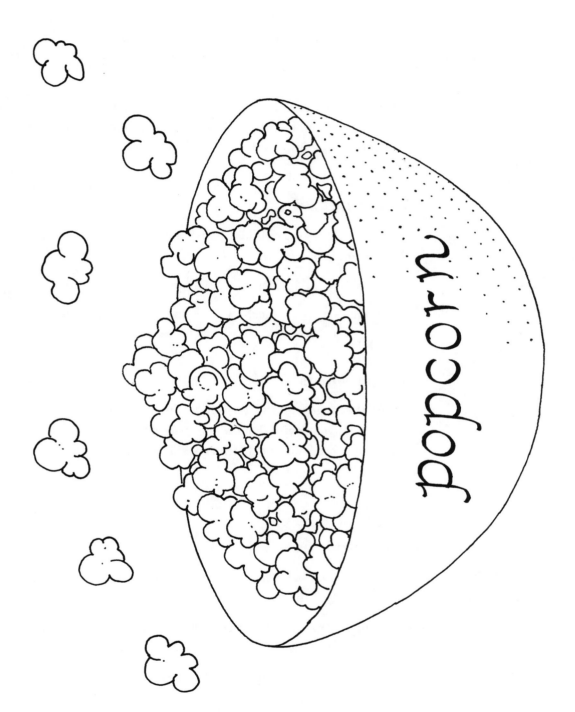

popcorn

**Paste the popcorn in the bowl.
Say "pop" for each popcorn you paste.**

Family Letter

Date: _____

Dear Family,

The emphasis in this lesson is on producing *p* at the beginning of words. When the *p* sound is produced, initially the airstream is completely blocked. The lips are closed lightly and then quickly separate as the breath escapes through the mouth with an explosive sound.

The book for this lesson is *Each Peach Pear Plum,* by Janet and Allan Ahlberg. It uses a rhyming "I Spy" game to make reference to familiar nursery rhymes and favorite stories. There are many words in the book to provide practice for *p* at the beginning of words.

Listening List

Read this list to your child. Slightly emphasize the *p* sound at the beginning of each word.

pea	pep	peep	pipe
pup	pickle	pear	plum
pen	pan		

Target Words

Using the pages in the speech folder, practice saying these words with your child. Follow the instructions provided at the end of this letter for any special considerations.

pie	pop
peach	pig

Suggested Home Activities

1. Read the story *Each Peach Pear Plum* to your child. Slightly emphasize the *p* sound at the beginning of the words *peach, pear,* and *pie.*

2. When grocery shopping, talk about different foods that begin with the *p* sound (e.g., *peach, pear, pie, pickle*).

3. Play with a toy puppy. Help your child say the word *puppy.*

4. Make popcorn together. Eat it, paste it on paper, or string it. Say the words *paper*, *paste*, and *popcorn*.

5. Make pudding together. Emphasize the word *pudding.*

6. Talk about the *Peach and Pear* art page that was painted. Help your child say the *p* sound in the words *peach, pear,* and *paint*.

7. Praise your child's work on the *Popcorn* art page. Help your child say the word *pop*.

Songs and Fingerplays

The following song and fingerplay are being practiced in class. You can help your child use the *p* sound by having him or her listen as you slightly emphasize the *p* sound at the beginning of the underlined words.

"<u>Pop</u> Goes the Weasel"

All around the mulberry bush.
The monkey chased the weasel.
The monkey thought it was all in fun.
<u>Pop</u> goes the weasel!

"<u>Pat-a-cake</u>"

<u>Pat-a-cake</u>, <u>pat-a-cake</u>, baker's man,
Bake me a cake as fast as you can;
<u>Pat</u> it and <u>pat</u> it, and mark it with P,
<u>Put</u> it in the oven for Baby and me.

Special Considerations

Sincerely,

_____

GOODNIGHT MOON

PATTERN

Prevocalic singleton

TARGET PHONEME

Word-initial /m/

TARGET WORDS

moon, mouse, mush, mitten

OPENING CENTER

GOAL

To introduce word-initial /m/

MATERIALS

Optional Materials
Bucket of objects such as a moon, a mouse, a mitten, a muffin, milk, meat, a map, a moose, a cow for "moo"

1. One set of alphabet letters (Appendix C)

2. Mirror

3. Book titled *Goodnight Moon* (1975), by Margaret Wise Brown

PROCEDURE

1. Introduce the letter *m* in the set of alphabet letters and demonstrate correct production of /m/. Sing the "Alphabet Song" (to the tune of "Twinkle, Twinkle, Little Star") and point to the letter *m* in the set of alphabet letters.

2. Have the children produce /m/ while looking in the mirror.

3. Introduce *Goodnight Moon*. Have the children take turns finger-tracing the letter *m* as you articulate /m/ in the title word *moon*.

4. Read *Goodnight Moon*. Model word-initial /m/ as it appears in the story (e.g., *moon, mouse, mitten*).

5. Sing the songs "Muffin Man" and "Old MacDonald Had a Farm."

   "Muffin Man"

   Oh, do you know the muffin man,
   the muffin man, the muffin man?
   Oh, do you know the muffin man,
   who lives on Muffin Lane?

   "Old MacDonald"

   Old MacDonald had a farm, E-I-E-I-O.
   And on that farm he had a cow, E-I-E-I-O.
   With a moo, moo here and a moo, moo there,
   here a moo, there a moo, everywhere a moo, moo,
   Old MacDonald had a farm, E-I-E-I-O.

   Old MacDonald had a farm, E-I-E-I-O.
   And on that farm he had a cat, E-I-E-I-O.
   With a meow, meow here and a meow, meow there,
   here a meow, there a meow, everywhere a meow, meow,
   Old MacDonald had a farm, E-I-E-I-O.

LISTENING CENTER

GOAL

To provide clear auditory stimuli for word-initial /m/

MATERIALS

1. One amplifier and one connector with headset per child

2. Listening list: *me, my, may, meat, muffin, miss, more, most, milk, must*

3. Illustrations of the four target words (pages 51–52; duplicate, cut out, and staple together)

4. Play dough

5. One bowl and spoon per child

Helpful Hints

For children having difficulty producing /m/, use the mirror to show them that the lips are closed. To facilitate nasality, it is often helpful to instruct the children to lightly place their fingers on the sides of their noses while they "hum." Children can often feel the vibration or the "motor" in their nose when this activity is introduced.

Optional Activity

Have the children close their eyes and reach into the bucket for an object. Model the name of each object, articulating the word-initial /m/. Have the children produce the word or word approximation

PROCEDURE

1. Instruct the children to wear their headsets and to listen. Speak into the amplifier and read the listening list to the children.

2. Introduce the four target words—*moon, mouse, mush, mitten*—to the children using the illustrations.

3. Instruct the children to continue wearing their headsets as you present a model of each target word. Have the children take turns repeating each word after it has been presented to each of them.

4. Help the children create a pretend mouse with some play dough. Then instruct the children to pretend to make mush using their bowl, spoon, and play dough. Have the children pretend to be the mouse and ask, "May I have some more mush please?" or "Mmm-mmm good!"

PRACTICE CENTER

GOAL

To facilitate production of word-initial /m/

Optional Materials

Mouse stickers, smelly stickers, or stickers that look like food

MATERIALS

1. One printed name card per child (see page 14)

2. Illustrations of the four target words (pages 51–52; duplicate, cut out, and staple together one set per child)

3. Colored markers

4. Each child's *Remediation Data Form* (Appendix B)

5. *Family Letter* (pages 55–56; duplicate one per child)

6. One speech folder per child

Optional Activity

Have the children choose a sticker to put on their folders and ask, "Whose sticker is this?" to elicit "Mine." You can also have the children say "Mmm-mmm good" for the stickers relating to smell or food.

PROCEDURE

1. Have the children find their own name card. Once identified, instruct the children to finger-trace and say the letters in their names.

2. Instruct the children to color the four target word illustrations—*moon, mouse, mush, mitten*—using the colored markers.

3. Have the children take turns naming the target word illustrations. The goal is to elicit word-initial /m/.

4. Document the children's productions on their *Remediation Data Form*.

5. Write notes related to each child's goal on his or her *Family Letter*.

ART CENTER

GOAL

To provide additional word-initial /m/ production practice and to create visual aids for home activities

MATERIALS

1. *Mama Animals* (page 53; duplicate one per child)

2. Crayons in a variety of colors

3. *Moon and Many Stars* (page 54; duplicate one per child)

4. Yellow and silver crayons

5. Blue watercolor paint

6. One paintbrush per child

PROCEDURE

Mama Animals

1. Help the children mark the mama animal with a crayon and color the baby animal the same color as the mama.

2. As the children are marking the mama animals, instruct them to say the name of the mama animal (e.g., *Mama Mouse, Mama Bear, Mama Bunny*).

3. Proceed in a similar fashion with all the animals.

4. Send this art page home in the child's speech folder.

Moon and Many Stars

1. Have the children use the crayons to color the moon yellow and the stars silver.

2. Using the watercolors, have the children paint the night sky blue. Children often enjoy painting over the crayon to give it an interesting look.

3. Elicit word-initial /m/ for the words *moon* and *many* as they paint the moon and the many stars.

4. Allow the art page to dry, and then send it home in the child's speech folder the following session.

Optional Snack Activity

At the end of the session, set out mini muffins. Have each child request a snack using a production based on his or her skill level.

HOME PRACTICE

GOAL

To provide home suggestions for what the children can do in the context of their everyday lives

MATERIALS

1. Each child's set of colored target word illustrations

2. Each child's completed art pages

3. Each child's speech folder

4. Each child's *Family Letter*

PROCEDURE

1. Collect the children's colored target word illustrations and completed art pages, and send them home in their speech folders.

2. Write any special instructions specific to a child on the *Family Letter*, on the target word illustrations, or on the art pages.

moon

mouse

mush

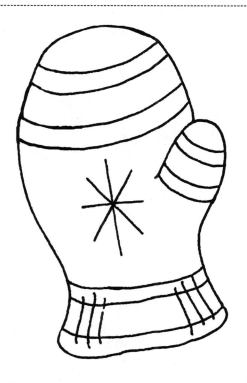

mitten

Mama Animals

Mama Cat

Mama Cow

Mama Mouse

Mama Bear

Mama Bunny

Mark the mama animals. Say the name of the mama animal. Then color the baby animals.

53

Paint the night sky blue.
Talk about the moon and the many stars.

Family Letter

Date: _____

Dear Family,

The emphasis in this lesson is on producing *m* at the beginning of words. When the *m* sound is produced, the lips are closed and the sound is produced through the nose.

The book for this lesson is *Goodnight Moon*, by Margaret Wise Brown. The book uses illustrations of the moon rising higher and higher as the room grows dimmer and dimmer to encourage children to use their own words for what they see. While reading the story to your child, identify words beginning with the *m* sound. It is also helpful to emphasize the rhyming words that appear throughout the story.

Listening List

Read this list to your child. Slightly emphasize the *m* sound at the beginning of each word.

me	my	may	meat
muffin	miss	more	most
milk	must		

Target Words

Using the pages in the speech folder, practice saying these words with your child. Follow the instructions provided at the end of this letter for any special considerations.

moon	mouse
mush	mitten

Suggested Home Activities

1. Read the story *Goodnight Moon* to your child. Slightly emphasize the *m* sound at the beginning of the words *moon, mouse,* and *mush*.

2. After reading *Goodnight Moon*, ask your child to find the mouse in each room scene. Help your child say the *m* sound in the word *mouse*. Point out the target words *moon, mouse,* and *mush*. Have your child listen carefully to the *m* sound at the beginning of the words.

3. Read nursery rhymes such as "Three Blind Mice," "Hickory, Dickory, Dock," and "Hey, Diddle, Diddle." Identify the *m* sound in words beginning with *m*.

4. At the dinner table, talk about pouring milk and cutting meat. Model the words *milk* and *meat*.

5. Have your child mail letters and bring in the mail. Slightly emphasize the *m* sound in the word *mail*.

6. Admire the artwork your child brings home. Help your child say the *m* sound in the word *moon*. Talk about each mama animal on the *Mama Animals* art page. Talk about the moon and the many stars in the sky on the *Moon and Many Stars* art page.

Songs

The following songs are being sung in class. You can help your child use the *m* sound by having him or her listen as you slightly emphasize the *m* sound at the beginning of the underlined words.

"<u>Muffin</u> <u>Man</u>"

Oh, do you know the <u>muffin</u> <u>man</u>,
the <u>muffin</u> <u>man</u>, the <u>muffin</u> <u>man</u>?
Oh, do you know the <u>muffin</u> <u>man</u>,
who lives on <u>Muffin</u> Lane?

"Old <u>MacDonald</u>"

Old <u>MacDonald</u> had a farm, E-I-E-I-O.
And on that farm he had a cow, E-I-E-I-O.
With a <u>moo</u>, <u>moo</u> here and a <u>moo</u>, <u>moo</u> there,
here a <u>moo</u>, there a <u>moo</u>, everywhere a <u>moo</u>, <u>moo</u>,
Old <u>MacDonald</u> had a farm, E-I-E-I-O.

Old <u>MacDonald</u> had a farm, E-I-E-I-O.
And on that farm he had a cat, E-I-E-I-O.
With a <u>meow</u>, <u>meow</u> here and a <u>meow</u>, <u>meow</u> there,
here a <u>meow</u>, there a <u>meow</u>, everywhere a <u>meow</u>, <u>meow</u>,
Old <u>MacDonald</u> had a farm, E-I-E-I-O.

Special Considerations

Sincerely,

_____

WHEELS ON THE BUS

PATTERN

Prevocalic singleton

TARGET PHONEME

Word-initial /w/

TARGET WORDS

windows, wipers, walk, one

OPENING CENTER

GOAL

To introduce word-initial /w/

MATERIALS

1. One set of alphabet letters (Appendix C)

2. Mirror

3. Book titled *Wheels on the Bus* (1988), by Raffi

> **Optional Materials**
>
> *Bucket of objects such as worms, a play bus to elicit "window," a watch, a [spider] web, water in a jar*

PROCEDURE

1. Introduce the letter *w* in the set of alphabet letters and demonstrate correct production of /w/. Sing the "Alphabet Song" (to the tune of "Twinkle, Twinkle, Little Star") and point to the letter *w* in the set of alphabet letters.

2. Have the children produce /w/ while looking in the mirror.

3. Introduce *Wheels on the Bus*. Point out the letter *w* in the title word *wheels*. Have the children take turns finger-tracing the letter *w* in the title word

wheels. (Because *wh* can be pronounced both /w/ and /hw/, *wheels* may or may not be an appropriate example of word-initial /w/. Use the wh-words in this lesson at your discretion.)

4. Read *Wheels on the Bus.* Model word-initial /w/ in the words *wheels, wipers,* and *wah.*

5. Sing the songs "Wheels on the Bus" and "Where is _____?"

"Wheels on the Bus"

The wheels on the bus go round and round,
round and round, round and round.
The wheels on the bus go round and round,
all around the town. *(Gesture a wheel going around.)*

The wipers on the bus go "swish, swish, swish..."
(Use your arms as wipers going back and forth.)

The driver on the bus goes "Move on back!..."
(Raise your arm and gesture a pushing back motion.)

The people on the bus go up and down...
(Move your body up and down.)

The horn on the bus goes "beep, beep, beep..."
(Use your hand to push a pretend horn.)

The baby on the bus goes "Wah, wah, wah..."
(Pretend to rub your eyes and cry.)

The parents on the bus go "Sh, sh, sh..."
(Gesture a quiet sound with your index finger at your lips.)

"Where is _____?"
(Sing to the tune of "Where is Thumbkin?" and fill in the blanks with children's names.)

ADULT: "Where is _____? Where is _____?"
(Hold your arms behind your back and have the children do the same.)

CHILD: "Here I am. Here I am."
(Bring your right arm out with thumb raised for "Here I am"; repeat with your left arm out and thumb raised for the second "Here I am.")

ADULT: "How are you today _____? How are you today _____?"
(Have your right thumb "talk" to your left thumb by wiggling it when asking the question; repeat with your left thumb "talking" to your right thumb.)

CHILD: "I am fine. I am fine."

LISTENING CENTER

GOAL

To provide clear auditory stimuli for word-initial /w/

MATERIALS

1. One amplifier and one connector with headset per child

2. Listening list: *win, wet, water, watch, wave, wind, worm, web, work, wipe*

3. Illustrations of the four target words (pages 63–64; duplicate, cut out, and staple together)

4. Play dough

PROCEDURE

1. Instruct the children to wear their headsets and to listen. Speak into the amplifier and read the listening list to the children.

2. Introduce the four target words—*windows, wipers, walk, one*—to the children using the illustrations.

3. Instruct the children to continue wearing their headsets as you present a model of each target word. Have the children take turns repeating each word after it has been presented to each of them.

4. Have the children use the play dough to make the numeral *1* and to make a worm. Model and have children repeat the words *one* and *worm*.

PRACTICE CENTER

GOAL

To facilitate production of word-initial /w/

MATERIALS

1. One printed name card per child (see page 14)

2. Illustrations of the four target words (pages 63–64; duplicate, cut out, and staple together one set per child)

3. Colored markers

Optional Materials

Stickers beginning with /w/ (e.g., worm or [spider] web stickers)

4. Each child's *Remediation Data Form* (Appendix B)

5. *Family Letter* (pages 67–68; duplicate one per child)

6. One speech folder per child

Optional Activity

Have the children choose a sticker to put on their folders and say, "This is a ___," omitting the name of the sticker to elicit the child's production of it.

PROCEDURE

1. Have the children find their own name card. Once identified, instruct the children to finger-trace and say the letters in their names.

2. Instruct the children to color the four target words illustrations—*windows, wipers, walk, one*—using the colored markers.

3. Have the children take turns naming the target word illustrations. The goal is to elicit word-initial /w/.

4. Document the children's productions on their *Remediation Data Forms*.

5. Write notes related to each child's goal on his or her *Family Letter*.

ART CENTER

GOAL

To provide additional word-initial /w/ production practice and to create visual aids for home activities

MATERIALS

1. *Bus Number 1* (page 65; duplicate one per child)

2. One yellow crayon per child

3. Orange watercolor paint

4. One paintbrush per child

5. *Concept of "One"* (page 66; duplicate one per child)

6. Crayons in a variety of colors

PROCEDURE

Bus Number 1

1. Have the children color the windows, wipers, wheels, and the number one using a yellow crayon. Model word-initial /w/ in the words *window, wheel, wiper,* and *one*. Instruct the children to round their lips when imitating the word-initial /w/ words.

2. Have the children use the watercolors to paint the bus orange. The yellow crayon will appear to highlight the items and words beginning with *w*. Elicit word-initial /w/ for the words *window, wipers, wheel,* and *one* as the children color and paint.

3. Allow the art page to dry, and then send it home in the child's speech folder the following session.

Concept of "One"

1. Count the crayons with the children. Teach the concept of "one" using the crayons.

2. Tell the children to choose one crayon. Model the word *one*.

3. Have the children point to the wheels on the page. Count the wheels with the children and point to one wheel. Have the children mark one wheel with a crayon. Have the children repeat the word *one*. Do the same procedure with the words *whales* and *windows*. Model the /w/ words for the children to repeat.

4. Send this art page home in the child's speech folder.

HOME PRACTICE

GOAL

To provide home suggestions for what the children can do in the context of their everyday lives

MATERIALS

1. Each child's set of colored target word illustrations

2. Each child's completed art pages

3. Each child's speech folder

4. Each child's *Family Letter*

PROCEDURE

1. Collect the children's colored target word illustrations and completed art pages, and send them home in their speech folders.

2. Write any special instructions specific to a child on the *Family Letter*, on the target word illustrations, or on the art pages.

windows

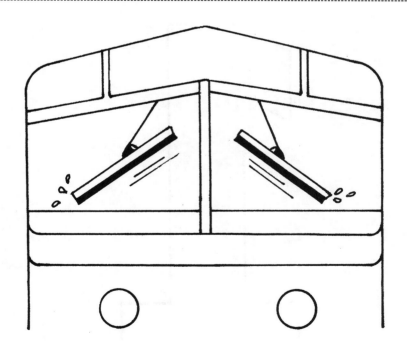

wipers

walk

one

Bus Number 1

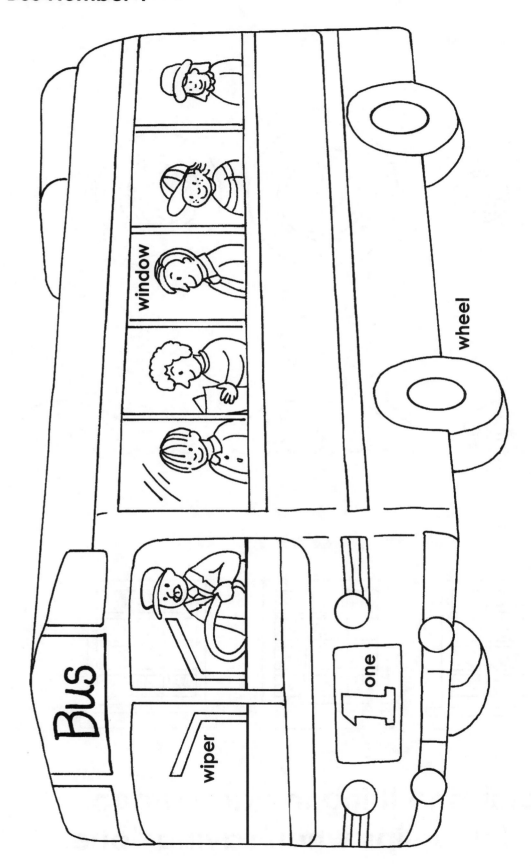

window

wheel

Bus

wiper

1 one

Color and paint the bus. Round your lips when saying "Window, wiper, and one."

Concept of "One"

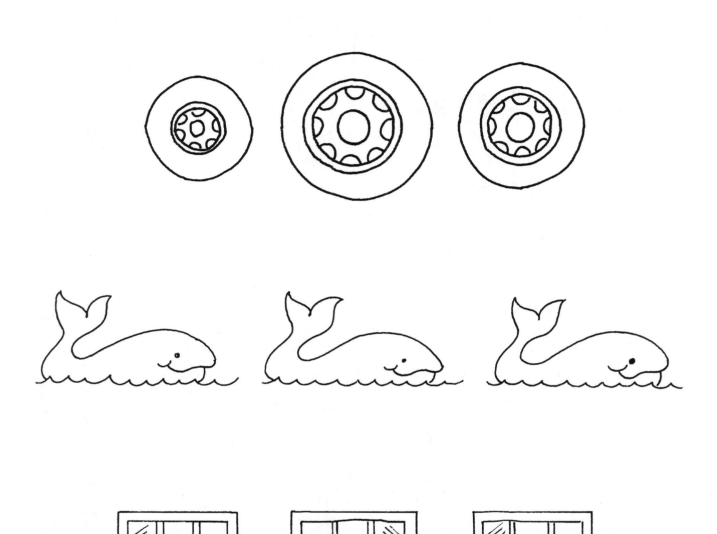

Color one thing in each group.
Round your lips when saying "one."

Family Letter

Date: _____

Dear Family,

The focus of this lesson is on producing *w* at the beginning of words. When the *w* sound is produced, the lips are rounded and the teeth are slightly separated. The index finger can be used to circle the lips to show they are round for the *w* sound.

The book for this lesson is *Wheels on the Bus,* by Raffi. It uses a song to help children articulate beginning sounds, especially the *w* sound.

Listening List

Read this list to your child. Slightly emphasize the *w* sound at the beginning of each word.

win	wet	water	watch
wave	wind	worm	web
work	wipe		

Target Words

Using the pages in the speech folder, practice saying these four words with your child. Follow the instructions provided at the end of this letter for any special considerations. (Even though the word *one* does not begin with *w*, it is appropriate as a target because of its functional use and high interest for young children.)

wipers	walk
one	windows

Suggested Home Activities

1. Read the story *Wheels on the Bus* to your child. Have your child watch you round your lips for words beginning with *w*. Have your child finger-trace the letter *w* in the word *wheels*.

2. Help your child count to five. Model the *w* sound in the word *one*.

3. Review the artwork your child brings home. Help your child understand the concept of "one." Point out the wheels on the bus and the wheels on your car. If your child does not correctly produce the *w* at the beginning of words, have him or her listen to the correct productions.

Songs

The following songs are being practiced in class. You can help your child use the *w* sound by having him or her listen as you slightly emphasize the *w* sound at the beginning of the underlined words.

"Wheels on the Bus"

The wheels on the bus go round and round,
round and round, round and round.
The wheels on the bus go round and round,
all around the town. *(Gesture a wheel going around.)*

The wipers on the bus go "swish, swish, swish…"
(Use your arms as wipers going back and forth.)

The driver on the bus goes "Move on back!…"
(Raise your arm and gesture a pushing back motion.)

The people on the bus go up and down…
(Move your body up and down.)

The horn on the bus goes "beep, beep, beep…"
(Use your hand to push a pretend horn.)

The baby on the bus goes "Wah, wah, wah…"
(Pretend to rub your eyes and cry.)

The parents on the bus go "Sh, sh, sh…"
(Gesture a quiet sound with your index finger at your lips.)

"Where is _____?"

(Sing to the tune of "Where is Thumbkin?" and fill in the blanks with your child's name.)

ADULT: "Where is _____? Where is _____?"
  (Hold your arms behind your back and have the children do the same.)

CHILD: "Here I am. Here I am."
  (Bring your right arm out with thumb raised for "Here I am"; repeat with your left arm out and thumb raised for the second "Here I am.")

ADULT: "How are you today _____? How are you today _____?"
  (Have your right thumb "talk" to your left thumb by wiggling it when asking the question; repeat with your left thumb "talking" to your right thumb.)

CHILD: "I am fine. I am fine."

Special Considerations

Sincerely,

_____

I WENT WALKING

PATTERN

Postvocalic singleton

TARGET PHONEME

Word-final /t/

TARGET WORDS

hat, night, wet, toot

OPENING CENTER

GOAL

To introduce word-final /t/

MATERIALS

1. One set of alphabet letters (Appendix C)

2. Mirror

3. Book titled *I Went Walking* (1990), by Sue Williams

4. One three-cornered hat per adult and per child made from three sheets of construction paper stapled together

5. One tongue depressor per child

Optional Materials
Bucket of objects such as a shirt, a boot, a robot, a rocket, a cat, a boat, a bat, a rabbit

PROCEDURE

1. Introduce the letter *t* from the set of alphabet letters and demonstrate correct production of /t/. Sing the "Alphabet Song" (to the tune of "Twinkle, Twinkle, Little Star") and point to the letter *t* from the set of alphabet letters.

2. Have the children produce /t/ while looking in the mirror.

3. Introduce *I Went Walking*. Point out the letter *t* in the title word *went*.

4. Read *I Went Walking*. Model word-final /t/ as it occurs in the story (e.g., *went, what, a lot, wet, cat*).

5. Say the fingerplays "My Hat, It Has Three Corners" and "I'm a Nut."

   "My Hat, It Has Three Corners"
   (Wear the hat and have each child wear a hat while singing this song.)

   My hat, it has three corners.
   (Touch the hat, hold up three fingers, then point to the corners on the hat.)
   Three corners has my hat.
   (Hold up three fingers; then touch the hat.)
   A hat without three corners
   could never be my hat.
   (Send the children's hats home in their speech folders.)

   "I'm a Nut"

   I'm an acorn small and round, lying on the cold, cold ground.
   (Make a fist with your hand and touch the ground with your fist.)
   People pass and step on me, that's why I'm all cracked, you see.
   (Stomp your foot when you say the word step.*)*
   I'm a nut *(clap, clap).*
   I'm a nut *(clap, clap).*
   I'm a nut *(clap, clap).*
   I'm a nut *(clap, clap).*

LISTENING CENTER

GOAL

To provide clear auditory stimuli for word-final /t/

MATERIALS

1. One amplifier and one connector with headset per child

2. Listening list: *out, knot, boat, bite, hot, eat, sit, boot, pet, tight*

3. Illustrations of the four target words (pages 74–75; duplicate, cut out, and staple together)

4. Play dough

5. One plastic knife per child

PROCEDURE

1. Instruct the children to wear their headsets and to listen. Speak into the amplifier and read the listening list to the children.

2. Introduce the four target words—*hat, night, wet, toot*—to the children using the illustrations.

3. Instruct the children to continue wearing their headsets as you present a model of each target word. Have the children take turns repeating each word after it has been presented to each of them.

4. Give each child play dough to roll into a snake. Have the children use the plastic knife to cut each snake into one long and one short piece. Model word-final /t/ in the word *cut*. Then have them form the letter *t* with the play dough pieces. Have the children pat the *t*. Model and elicit word-final /t/ in the word *pat*.

PRACTICE CENTER

GOAL

To facilitate production of word-final /t/

MATERIALS

<table>
<tr><td></td><td>Optional Materials</td></tr>
</table>

Stickers ending with /t/ (e.g, robot, hat, boat, or carrot stickers)

1. One printed name card per child (see page 14)

2. Illustrations of the four target words (pages 74–75; duplicate, cut out, and staple together one set per child)

3. Colored markers

4. Each child's *Remediation Data Form* (Appendix B)

5. *Family Letter* (pages 78–79; duplicate one per child)

6. One speech folder per child

PROCEDURE

1. Have the children find their own name card. Once identified, instruct the children to finger-trace and say the letters in their names.

2. Instruct the children to color the four target word illustrations—*hat, night, wet, toot*—using the colored markers.

3. Have the children take turns naming the target word illustrations. The goal is to elicit word-final /t/.

4. Document the children's productions on their *Remediation Data Forms*.

5. Write notes related to each child's goal on his or her *Family Letter*.

ART CENTER

GOAL

To provide additional word-initial /t/ production practice and to create visual aids for home activities

MATERIALS

1. *Paint a Boat* (page 76; duplicate one per child)

2. A variety of watercolor paints

3. One paintbrush per child

4. *Dot Art* (page 77; duplicate one per child)

5. One colored pencil per child (any color)

PROCEDURE

Paint a Boat

1. Have the children paint each boat a different color.

2. While the children paint each boat, model and elicit word-final /t/ in the words *boat* and *paint*.

3. Allow the art page to dry, and then send it home in the child's speech folder the following session.

Dot Art

1. Demonstrate for the children how to make a dot on a picture.

2. Have the children put a dot on each treat they like to eat.

3. Model and elicit word-final /t/ in the words *dot*, *eat,* and *treat*. Talk about what the children like to eat and what they don't like to eat.

4. Send this art page home in the child's speech folder.

Optional Activity

Have the children choose a sticker to put on their folders. Ask specific questions to facilitate production of word-final /t/ (e.g., ask "What floats in the water?" to elicit "A boat").

HOME PRACTICE

GOAL

To provide home suggestions for what the children can do in the context of their everyday lives

MATERIALS

1. Each child's set of colored target word illustrations

2. Each child's completed art pages

3. Each child's three-cornered hat

4. Each child's speech folder

5. Each child's *Family Letter*

PROCEDURE

1. Collect the children's colored target word illustrations, completed art pages, and three-cornered hat, and send them home in their speech folders.

2. Write any special instructions specific to a child on the *Family Letter*, on the target word illustrations, or on the art pages.

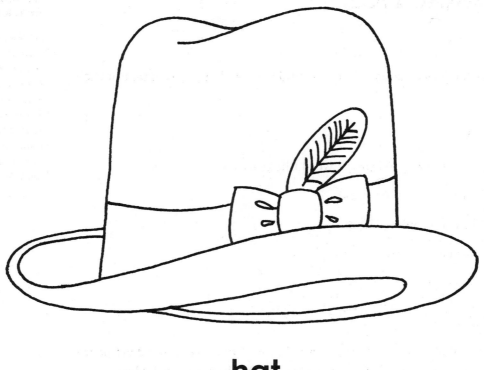

hat

night

wet

toot

Paint the boats. Talk about what you painted (a boat, a blue boat, etc.).

Put a dot on each treat.
Talk about what you like to eat and
what you don't like to eat.

Family Letter

Date: _____

Dear Family,

Sometimes children omit the final sounds in words. The emphasis for this lesson is on producing *t* at the end of words. The *t* sound is made by placing the tip of the tongue behind the upper front teeth with the sides of the tongue against the side teeth. There is a quick release of the tongue tip, which produces the explosion of sound.

The book for this lesson is *I Went Walking,* by Sue Williams. Words with the final *t* sound are repeated in this story (e.g., "I *went* walking." "*What* did you see?"). By hearing the final *t* in words, children begin to understand that most words have a consonant sound at the end.

Listening List

Read this list to your child. Slightly emphasize the *t* sound at the end of each word.

out	knot	boat	bite
hot	eat	sit	boot
pet	tight		

Target Words

Using the pages in the speech folder, practice saying these words with your child. Follow the instructions provided at the end of this letter for any special considerations.

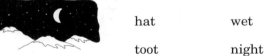

| hat | wet |
| toot | night |

Suggested Home Activities

1. Read the story *I Went Walking* to your child. Emphasize the *t* sound at the end of the words *went* and *what*.

2. Pot a plant in a flower pot. Slightly emphasize the final *t* sound in the words *pot* and *plant*.

3. Squirt shaving cream in a tray. Make a hand print. Model the word *print*.

4. Use pretend foods and eat together. Model the word *eat*.

5. Collect different hats for imaginary play. Talk about a blue hat, a cowboy hat, etc. Help your child say the final *t* sound in the word *hat*.

6. Admire the *Paint a Boat* art page your child brings home. Help your child say the final *t* sound in the words *boat* and *paint*. Have your child tell you about the color of each boat (a black boat, a red boat).

7. Review the *Dot Art* page. Talk about each treat that has a dot on it. Help your child say the *t* sound in *dot*, *eat,* and *treat*.

Fingerplays

The following fingerplays are being practiced in class. You can help your child use the *t* sound by having him or her listen as you slightly emphasize the *t* sound at the end of the underlined words.

"My Hat, It Has Three Corners"
(Put the three-cornered hat on your child's head before saying this finger-play.)

My hat, it has three corners.
(Touch the hat, hold up three fingers, then point to the corners on the hat.)
Three corners has my hat.
(Hold up three fingers; then touch the hat.)
A hat without three corners
could never be my hat.

"I'm a Nut"

I'm an acorn small and round, lying on the cold, cold ground.
(Make a fist with your hand and touch the ground with your fist.)
People pass and step on me, that's why I'm all cracked, you see.
(Stomp your foot when you say the word step.*)*
I'm a nut *(clap, clap).*
I'm a nut *(clap, clap).*
I'm a nut *(clap, clap).*
I'm a nut *(clap, clap).*

Special Considerations

Sincerely,

SHAKE MY SILLIES OUT

PATTERN

Postvocalic singleton

TARGET PHONEME

Word-final /k/

TARGET WORDS

knock, walk, back, hook

OPENING CENTER

GOAL

To introduce word-final /k/

Optional Materials
Bucket of objects such as a bike, a hook, a fork, a book, a sock, a milk carton, a snake, a truck, a lock, a block, a rock, a duck

MATERIALS

1. One set of alphabet letters (Appendix C)

2. Picture of a crow

3. Book titled *Shake My Sillies Out* (1987), by Raffi

4. One tongue depressor per child

PROCEDURE

1. Introduce the letter *k* in the set of alphabet letters and demonstrate correct production of /k/. Have the children feel your throat while you produce /k/. Sing the "Alphabet Song" (to the tune of "Twinkle, Twinkle, Little Star") and point to the letter *k* in the set of alphabet letters.

2. Help each child produce /k/. Some children can produce /k/ in the word *caw*, using an elevated pitch. Show a picture of a crow, and model *caw, caw* in a high pitch. Tell the children /k/ is Kenny the Crow's "caw caw" sound.

3. Introduce *Shake My Sillies Out*. Point out the letter *k* in the title word *shake*.

4. Read *Shake My Sillies Out*. Model word-final /k/ in the words *shake, park,* and *dark*.

5. Sing the song "Shake My Sillies Out" and say the fingerplay "Bumble Bee."

"Shake My Sillies Out"

(Shake your hands when singing.)

Gotta shake, shake, shake my sillies out,
shake, shake, shake my sillies out,
shake, shake, shake my sillies out,
and wiggle my waggles away.

"Bumble Bee"

I'm bringing home a baby bumble bee.
(Cup your hands together.)
Won't my mommy be so proud of me.
I'm bringing home a baby bumble bee.
YICK! It stung me.
(Make a distraught face and point to a pretend bee sting.)

I'm smashing up my baby bumble bee.
(Smash hands together.)
Won't my mommy be so proud of me.
I'm smashing up my baby bumble bee.
YUK! It's yucky!
(Exaggerate the unpleasantness.)

I'm wiping up my baby bumble bee.
(Wipe your hands together.)
Won't my mommy be so proud of me?
I'm wiping up my baby bumble bee.
LOOK!
(Outstretch your arms.)
My mommy's proud of me!
(Make a big smile.)

Helpful Hints

- *Some children can make an approximation of /k/ by "coughing" and directing attention to the back part of the throat.*

- *Sometimes /k/ may be secured by developing it from /ŋ/.*

- *It may be necessary to hold down the tip of the tongue with the tongue depressor while the child attempts to produce /k/.*

- *Cue /k/ by pushing under the chin with two fingers.*

Optional Activity

Have the children close their eyes and reach into the bucket to feel an object. While feeling the object, the children should guess what they think the object might be. Ask "What do you think it is?" After the children make a guess and pull the object from the bucket, model the name of the object, articulating word-final /k/. Elicit the name of the object from the children as a whole word or as a segmented word (e.g., "hoo...k").

LISTENING CENTER

GOAL

To provide clear auditory stimuli for word-final /k/

Optional Materials

Biscuit cutters and cookie cutters shaped like the letter k

MATERIALS

1. One amplifier and one connector with headset per child

2. Listening list: *look, talk, book, bike, stack, pack, neck, rock, lick, shake*

3. Illustrations of the four target words (pages 85–86; duplicate, cut out, and staple together)

4. Play dough

5. One popsicle stick per child

Optional Activity

Using the play dough and biscuit cutters, help the children make a pretend cake. Elicit word-final /k/ in the word cake. *Use the letter* k *cookie cutter to make the letter* k *out of play dough. Elicit /k/.*

PROCEDURE

1. Instruct the children to wear their headsets and to listen. Speak into the amplifier and read the listening list to the children.

2. Introduce the four target words—*knock, walk, back, hook*—to the children using the illustrations.

3. Instruct the children to continue wearing their headsets as you present a model of each target word. Have the children take turns repeating each word after it has been presented to each of them.

4. Help the children create a pretend animal with the play dough. Have the children "shake the sillies out" of their animals. Elicit word-final /k/ in the word *shake*. Have the children walk their animals and elicit word-final /k/ in the word *walk*.

5. Have the children make lollipops from play dough and popsicle sticks and then pretend to lick them. Elicit word-final /k/ in the word *lick*.

PRACTICE CENTER

GOAL

To facilitate production of word-final /k/

MATERIALS

1. One printed name card per child (see page 14)

2. Illustrations of the four target words (pages 85–86; duplicate, cut out, and staple together one set per child)

3. Colored markers

4. Each child's *Remediation Data Form* (Appendix B)

5. *Family Letter* (pages 89–90; duplicate one per child)

6. One speech folder per child

Optional Materials

Stickers ending with /k/ (e.g., [birthday] cake or bike stickers)

PROCEDURE

1. Have the children find their own name card. Once identified, instruct the children to finger-trace and say the letters in their names.

2. Instruct the children to color the four target word illustrations—*knock, walk, back, hook*—using the colored markers.

3. Have the children take turns naming the target word illustrations. The goal is to elicit word-final /k/.

4. Document the children's productions on their *Remediation Data Forms*.

5. Write notes related to each child's goal on his or her *Family Letter*.

Optional Activity

Have the children choose a sticker to put on their folders. Make a statement to elicit production of word-final /k/ (e.g., "On your birthday everyone sings 'Happy Birthday' and then you get to blow out the candles on your _____").

ART CENTER

GOAL

To provide additional word-initial /k/ production practice and to create visual aids for home activities

MATERIALS

1. *Animal Shake* (page 87; duplicate one per child)

2. Glue

3. Glitter

4. *Walk, Talk, and Chalk* (page 88; duplicate one per child)

5. Colored chalk

PROCEDURE

Animal Shake

1. Help the children outline each animal with glue.

2. Have the children shake glitter on the glue. Point out to the children that the curvy art lines near the animals indicate that the animals are moving. Elicit the word *shake* from each child.

3. Allow the art page to dry, and then send it home in the child's speech folder the following session.

Walk, Talk, and Chalk

1. Show the children the different colors of chalk. Model word-final /k/ in the word *chalk*.

2. Have the children use different colored chalk to color each word that ends in word-final /k/. Elicit word-final /k/ in the various words. Aim for correct production of /k/ at the ends of words.

3. Send this art page home in the child's speech folder.

<table>
<tr><td>

Optional Snack Activity

At the end of the session, set out Tic Tacs or Slo-Pokes. Have each child request a snack using a production based on his or her skill level.

</td><td>

HOME PRACTICE

GOAL

To provide home suggestions for what the children can do in the context of their everyday lives

MATERIALS

1. Each child's set of colored target word illustrations

2. Each child's completed art pages

3. Each child's speech folder

4. Each child's *Family Letter*

PROCEDURE

1. Collect the children's colored target word illustrations and completed art pages, and send them home in their speech folders.

2. Write any special instructions specific to a child on the *Family Letter*, on the target word illustrations, or on the art pages.

</td></tr>
</table>

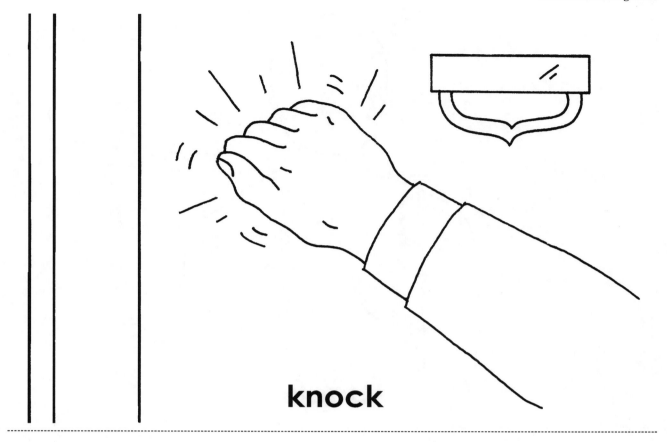

knock

walk

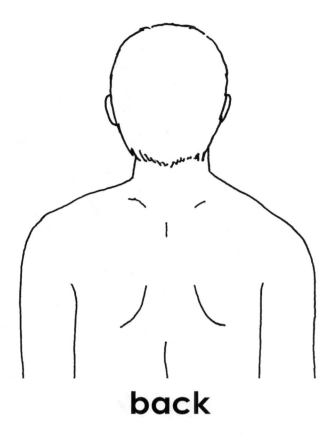

back

- -

hook

Shake glitter on the animals.
Talk about what these animals do.

Walk, Talk, and Chalk

bike

peek

rock

book

sidewalk

walk

Color the pictures that end with "k." Name each picture you colored.

Family Letter

Date: _____

Dear Family,

In this lesson, the focus is on the *k* sound at the end of words. Children appear to have better success learning the *k* sound when it occurs at the end of a word rather than at the beginning of the word. There are two movements involved when making the *k* sound. First, the back portion of the tongue is raised and makes contact with the front portion of the soft palate. Second, the back part of the tongue is suddenly lowered and breath escapes with an explosive sound. Some children find this sound quite challenging to produce. We call the *k* sound the Kenny the Crow "caw caw" sound.

For this lesson, the story and song by Raffi called *Shake My Sillies Out* is used. The children love to hear this song with its accompanying actions, and they quickly become familiar with the *k* sound in the word *shake*.

Listening List

Read this list to your child. Slightly emphasize the *k* sound at the end of each word.

look	talk	book	bike
stack	pack	neck	rock
lick	shake		

Target Words

Using the pages in the speech folder, practice saying these words with your child. Follow the instructions provided at the end of this letter for any special considerations.

knock	back
walk	hook

Suggested Home Activities

1. Read the story *Shake My Sillies Out* to your child. Slightly emphasize the *k* sound at the end of the word *shake*.

2. Play "Peek-a-Boo." Model the *k* sound in the word *peek*, and have your child repeat it.

3. Tell your child you are going to look for a rock. Model the *k* sound in the words *look* and *rock*.

4. Review the *Animal Shake* art page. Help your child say the *k* sound at the end the word *shake*. Ask your child to tell you what he or she used to color the animals (chalk).

5. Review the *Walk, Talk, and Chalk* art page. Help your child name each picture ending with the *k* sound.

Songs and Fingerplays

The following song and fingerplay are being practiced in class. You can help your child use the *k* sound by having him or her listen as you slightly emphasize the *k* sound at the end of the underlined words.

"<u>Shake</u> My Sillies Out"
(Shake your hands when singing.)

Gotta <u>shake</u>, <u>shake</u>, <u>shake</u> my sillies out,
<u>shake</u>, <u>shake</u>, <u>shake</u> my sillies out,
<u>shake</u>, <u>shake</u>, <u>shake</u> my sillies out,
and wiggle my waggles away.

"Bumble Bee"

I'm bringing home a baby bumble bee.
(Cup your hands together.)
Won't my mommy be so proud of me.
I'm bringing home a baby bumble bee.
<u>YICK</u>! It stung me.
(Make a distraught face and point to a pretend bee sting.)

I'm smashing up my baby bumble bee.
(Smash hands together.)
Won't my mommy be so proud of me.
I'm smashing up my baby bumble bee.
<u>YUK</u>! It's yucky!
(Exaggerate the unpleasantness.)

I'm wiping up my baby bumble bee.
(Wipe your hands together.)
Won't my mommy be so proud of me?
I'm wiping up my baby bumble bee.
<u>LOOK</u>!
(Outstretch your arms.)
My mommy's proud of me!
(Make a big smile.)

Special Considerations

Sincerely,

_____

PRIMARY TARGET PATTERNS: ANTERIOR/ POSTERIOR CONTRASTS

MOO MOO, BROWN COW

PATTERN

Velars

TARGET PHONEME

Word-final /k/

TARGET WORDS

lock, kick, rock, book

OPENING CENTER

GOAL

To introduce word-final /k/

MATERIALS

1. One set of alphabet letters (Appendix C)

2. Book titled *Moo Moo, Brown Cow* (1992), by Jakki Wood

PROCEDURE

1. Introduce the letter *k* in the set of alphabet letters and demonstrate correct production of /k/. Sing the "Alphabet Song" (to the tune of "Twinkle, Twinkle, Little Star") and point to the letter *k* in the set of alphabet letters. (If appropriate, also point out that the letter *c* can sometimes make /k/.)

2. Model /k/. Then instruct the children to imitate /k/. If they are successful producing /k/ in isolation, instruct the children to imitate word-final /k/ in a vowel-consonant production (e.g., /ɪk/, /æk/).

> **Optional Materials**
>
> *Bucket of objects such as a duck for "quack," a hen for "cluck," a frog for "croak," a chick, a sock, a cake, a yak, a tack, a bike*

3. Read *Moo Moo, Brown Cow.* Model word-final /k/ in the words *duck, chick, oink,* etc. Elicit word-final /k/ as appropriate with each child.

4. Say the rhyme "Jack and Jill" and the fingerplay the "Ten Little Ducklings."

"Jack and Jill"

Jack and Jill went up the hill to fetch a pail of water.
Jack fell down and broke his crown and Jill came tumbling after.

"Ten Little Ducklings"

Ten little ducklings,
(Hold up your hands with your fingers spread out.)
dash, dash, dash!
(Move your fingers back and forth.)
Jumped in the duck pond,
(Move your hands downward.)
splash, splash, splash!
(Pretend to splash water.)
When the mother called them,
(Put your hand at your mouth as if it were the duck's beak.)
quack, quack, quack!
(Open and close your hand in unison.)
Ten little ducklings came right back.
(Hold up your hands and move your fingers back and forth.)

LISTENING CENTER

GOAL

To provide clear auditory stimuli for word-final /k/

MATERIALS

1. One amplifier and one connector with headset per child

2. Listening list: *park, suck, sock, quack, cluck, croak, chick, black, brick, sick*

3. Illustrations of the four target words (pages 98–99; duplicate, cut out, and staple together)

4. Play dough

PROCEDURE

1. Instruct the children to wear their headsets and to listen. Speak into the amplifier and read the listening list to the children.

2. Introduce the four target words—*lock, kick, rock, book*—to the children using the illustrations.

3. Instruct the children to continue wearing their headsets as you present a model of each target word. Have the children take turns repeating each word after it has been presented to each of them.

PRACTICE CENTER

GOAL

To facilitate production of word-final /k/

MATERIALS

1. One printed name card per child (see page 14)

2. Illustrations of the four target words (pages 98–99; duplicate, cut out, and staple together one set per child)

3. Colored markers

4. Each child's *Remediation Data Form* (Appendix B)

5. *Family Letter* (pages 102–103; duplicate one per child)

6. One speech folder per child

PROCEDURE

1. Have the children find their own name card. Once identified, instruct the children to finger-trace and say the letters in their names.

2. Instruct the children to color the four target word illustrations—*lock, kick, rock, book*—using the colored markers.

3. Have the children take turns naming the target word illustrations. The goal is to elicit word-final /k/.

4. Document the children's productions on their *Remediation Data Forms*.

5. Write notes related to each child's goal on his or her *Family Letter*.

Optional Activity

Using the play dough and the cookie cutters, help the children cut out ducks, pigs, frogs, or chickens. Practice making the appropriate animal sound ("quack, quack," "oink, oink," "croak, croak," or "cluck, cluck").

Optional Materials

Stickers ending with /k/ (e.g., a duck sticker)

Optional Activity

Have the children choose a sticker to put on their folders. Then talk or ask questions about the sticker to elicit word-final /k/ productions (e.g., "What is this?" to elicit "Duck" or "The duck says _____ to elicit

ART CENTER

GOAL

To provide additional word-final /k/ production practice and to create visual aids for home activities

MATERIALS

1. *Play "Peek!"* (page 100; duplicate one per child)

2. Crayons

3. One scissors per child

4. Four popsicle sticks per child

5. Stapler

6. *At the Park* (page 101; duplicate one per child)

7. One colored pencil per child

PROCEDURE

Play "Peek!"

1. Instruct the children to color the animals using the crayons.

2. Model word-final /k/ in the words *cluck, chick, croak,* and *quack,* and have the children repeat the words.

3. Help the children use the scissors to cut out the circles. Then staple each to a popsicle stick to form stick puppets.

4. Play "Peek!" by holding up a stick puppet and saying, "Peek-a-puppet! The (duck) says ____" to elicit, for example, "Quack, quack." Repeat with other stick puppets. Then allow the children to play with the stick puppets, making animal sounds with others in the group.

5. Send the stick puppets home in the child's speech folder.

At the Park

1. Give each child a colored pencil.

2. Name an object for the child to find in the picture (e.g., a book, a bike). Model the word-final /k/ in each word.

3. Instruct the children to color the picture named using the colored pencil.

4. Help the children say the word-final /k/ pictures they have colored.

5. Send this art page home in each child's speech folder.

HOME PRACTICE

Optional Snack Activity

At the end of the session, set out some small cups of Coke. Have each child request the Coke based on his or her skill level.

GOAL

To provide home suggestions for what the children can do in the context of their everyday lives

MATERIALS

1. Each child's set of colored target word illustrations

2. Each child's completed art page and stick puppets

3. Each child's speech folder

4. Each child's *Family Letter*

PROCEDURE

1. Collect the children's colored target word illustrations, completed art page, and stick puppets, and send them home in their speech folders.

2. Write any special instructions specific to a child on the *Family Letter*, on the target word illustrations, or on the art page.

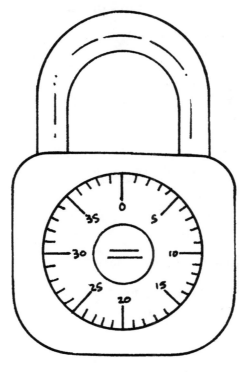

lock

kick

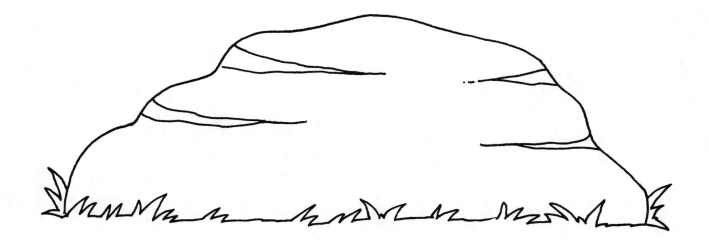

rock

book

Color and cut out each circle
to make stick puppets.

At the Park

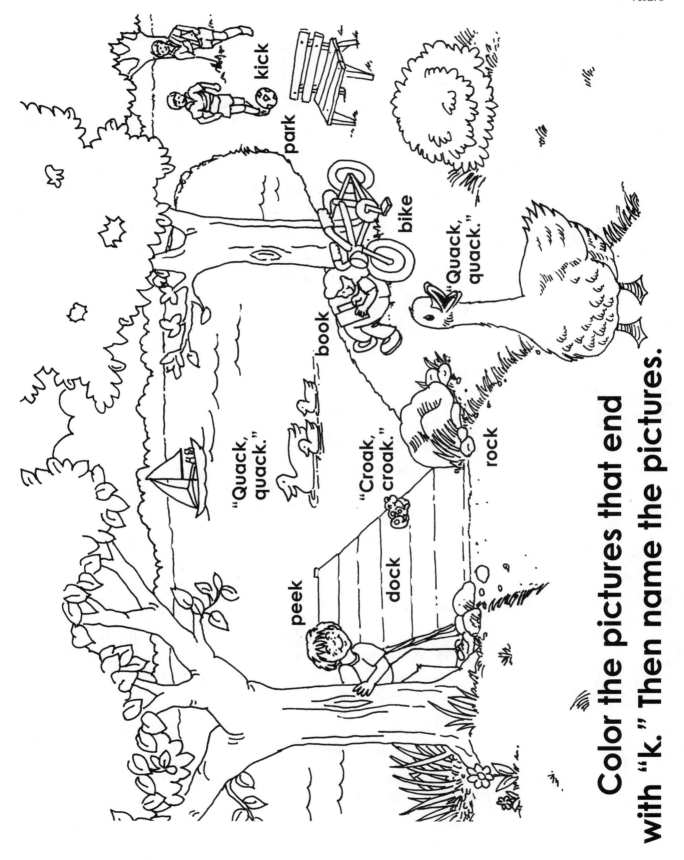

kick

park

bike

book

"Quack, quack."

"Quack, quack."

"Croak, croak."

peek

dock

rock

Color the pictures that end with "k." Then name the pictures.

Family Letter

Date: _____

Dear Family,

Children with delays in learning to say sounds sometimes omit the final conso-nant in words. It is also common for these children to incorrectly produce the *k* and *g* sounds, especially at the end of words. To help children learn to produce the final consonant in words, we will focus on the *k* sound.

To produce the *k* sound, the back part of the tongue is raised and makes contact with the soft palate. It's then lowered with a quick release of breath. The book *Moo Moo, Brown Cow,* by Jakki Wood, provides many opportunities for children to hear and practice the final *k* in words (e.g., *honk, quack, chick, cluck, oink, pink,* and *croak*).

Listening List

Read this list to your child. Slightly emphasize the *k* at the end of each word.

park	suck	sock	quack
honk	cluck	oink	croak
chick	duck		

Target Words

Using the pages in the speech folder, practice saying these words with your child. Follow the instructions provided at the end of this letter for any special considerations.

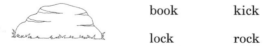

book	kick
lock	rock

Suggested Home Activities

1. Read the story *Moo Moo, Brown Cow* to your child. Slightly emphasize the *k* sound at the end of the words *pink, black, duck, honk, cluck, oink, croak.* If your child imitates your *k* productions in words, provide some practice saying the words in the story.

2. Go to a park. Talk about the words *park, duck, quack, honk, rock,* etc.

3. Play "Peek-a-Boo!" slightly emphasizing the word *peek.*

4. Sing "Old MacDonald Had a Farm" using animal sounds, such as "oink, oink" and "quack, quack."

5. Have your child look at objects through a paper towel tube. Help him or her say *look* while looking.

6. Use the stick puppets to play with your child. Slightly emphasize the *k* sound at the end of the words *cluck, croak, chick,* and *quack.*

7. Admire the *At the Park* art page your child brings home. Talk about the words in the picture that end with the *k* sound.

Rhymes and Fingerplays

The following rhyme and fingerplay are being practiced in class. You can help your child use the *k* sound by having him or her listen as you slightly exaggerate the *k* sound at the end of the underlined words.

"Jack and Jill"

Jack and Jill went up the hill to fetch a pail of water.
Jack fell down and broke his crown and Jill came tumbling after.

"Ten Little Ducklings"

Ten little ducklings,
(Hold up your hands with your fingers spread out.)
dash, dash, dash!
(Move your fingers back and forth.)
Jumped in the duck pond,
(Move your hands downward.)
splash, splash, splash!
(Pretend to splash water.)
When the mother called them,
(Put your hand at your mouth as if it were the duck's beak.)
quack, quack, quack!
(Open and close your hand in unison.)
Ten little ducklings came right back.
(Hold up your hands and move your fingers back and forth.)

Special Considerations

Sincerely,

_____

I AM KING

PATTERN

Velars

TARGET PHONEME

Word-initial /k/

TARGET WORDS

king, comb, cake, cub

OPENING CENTER

GOAL

To introduce word-initial /k/

Optional Materials

Bucket of objects such as a king (from a deck of cards), a comb, a cane, a cake, a can of Coke, a kite, a cub, candy

MATERIALS

1. One set of alphabet letters (Appendix C)

2. One brightly colored feather

3. Book titled *I Am King* (1994), by Mary Packard

4. One tongue depressor per child

PROCEDURE

1. Introduce the letter *k* in the set of alphabet letters and demonstrate correct production of /k/. Sing the "Alphabet Song" (to the tune of "Twinkle, Twinkle, Little Star") and point to the letter *k* in the set of alphabet letters. (If appropriate, also point out that the letter *c* can sometimes make /k/.)

2. Hold the brightly colored feather in front of your mouth and produce /k/. This will demonstrate the explosive release of /k/. Hold the feather in front of each child's mouth, and have him or her produce /k/.

3. Introduce *I Am King*. Point out the letter *k* in the title word *king*.

4. Read *I Am King*. Model word-initial /k/ in the words *king, come,* and *crown*.

5. Sing the song "She'll Be Comin' 'Round the Mountain" and say the rhyme "Old King Cole."

"She'll Be Comin' 'Round the Mountain"

She'll be comin' 'round the mountain when she comes.
She'll be comin' 'round the mountain when she comes.
She'll be comin' 'round the mountain,
she'll be comin' 'round the mountain,
she'll be comin' 'round the mountain when she comes.

"Old King Cole"

Old King Cole was a merry old soul,
and a merry old soul was he.
He called for his cap and he called for his comb,
and he called for his candy canes three.

LISTENING CENTER

GOAL

To provide clear auditory stimuli for word-initial /k/

MATERIALS

1. One amplifier and one connector with headset per child

2. Listening list: *cannon, cola, cough, castle, carry, cool, kitten, cane, color, candy*

3. Illustrations of the four target words (pages 109–110; duplicate, cut out, and staple together)

4. Play dough

5. One birthday candle per child

6. One small comb per child

Helpful Hints

Use the tongue depressor to gently hold down the tip of a child's tongue, thus allowing the elevation of the back of the tongue when /k/ is produced. It is also effective to use your index and middle finger to form a "V" shape and then push up on the neck. Having some children "cough" to produce /k/, which assists in directing attention to the back of the throat, is also effective.

Optional Activity

Have the children close their eyes and reach into the bucket for an object. Model the name of the object, articulating word-initial /k/. Have the children produce the word or word approximation after your model.

PROCEDURE

1. Instruct the children to wear their headsets and to listen. Speak into the amplifier and read the listening list to the children.

2. Introduce the four target words—*king, comb, cake, cub*—to the children using the illustrations.

3. Instruct the children to continue wearing their headsets as you present a model of each target word. Have the children take turns repeating each word after it has been presented to each of them.

4. Demonstrate how to make a small birthday cake out of the play dough. Help the children each make a cake and place a candle in their cakes. Elicit the words *cake* and *candle* as appropriate with each child.

5. Help the children shape a cookie from the play dough. Have the children use the comb to make designs on the cookies. Elicit word-initial /k/ in the words *comb* and *cookie*.

PRACTICE CENTER

GOAL

To facilitate production of word-initial /k/

Optional Materials
Stickers beginning with /k/ (e.g., candy or "cool" stickers)

MATERIALS

1. One printed name card per child (see page 14)

2. Illustrations of the four target words (pages 109–110; duplicate, cut out, and staple together one set per child)

3. Colored markers

4. Each child's *Remediation Data Form* (Appendix B)

5. *Family Letter* (pages 113–114; duplicate one per child)

6. One speech folder per child

PROCEDURE

1. Have the children find their own name card. Once identified, instruct the children to finger-trace and say the letters in their names.

2. Have the children color the four target word illustrations—*king, comb, cake, cub*—using the colored markers.

3. Have the children take turns naming the target word illustrations. The goal is to elicit word-initial /k/.

4. Document the children's productions on their *Remediation Data Forms*.

5. Write notes related to each child's goal on his or her *Family Letter*.

Optional Activity

Have the children choose a sticker to put on their folders. Then talk or ask questions about the sticker to elicit word-initial /k/ productions (e.g., "What kind of sticker did you choose?" to elicit "A candy cane").

ART CENTER

GOAL

To provide additional word-initial /k/ production practice and to create visual aids for home activities

MATERIALS

1. *King's Castle* (page 111; duplicate one per child)

2. One crayon per child

3. *Cool Food* (page 112; duplicate one per child)

4. Soft crayons (Craypas)

PROCEDURE

King's Castle

1. Name the word-initial /k/ pictures for the children and relate the pictures to the story *I Am King*. Elicit /k/ productions as appropriate for each child. (Note that the focus is on the word *king* for "king's cloak" and "king's ring.")

2. Have the children use the crayon to draw a line along the path to each clue and then color the picture. Model and elicit word-initial /k/ in the clue words and have each child repeat the words as appropriate for his or her skill level.

3. Send this art page home in the child's speech folder.

Cool Food

1. Name the food and elicit /k/ in isolation and/or in the word as appropriate for each child.

2. Have the children color the food with soft crayons.

3. Have the children point to the food they like. If appropriate, elicit the word-final /k/ word in the sentence "I like ___."

4. Send this art page home in the child's speech folder.

Optional Snack Activity

At the end of the session, set out a small snack beginning with /k/ (e.g., carrots, cookies, cocoa, or cola). Have each child request a snack using a production based on his or her skill level.

HOME PRACTICE

GOAL

To provide home suggestions for what the children can do in the context of their everyday lives

MATERIALS

1. Each child's set of colored target word illustrations

2. Each child's completed art pages

3. Each child's speech folder

4. Each child's *Family Letter*

PROCEDURE

1. Collect the children's colored target word illustrations and completed art pages, and send them home in their speech folders.

2. Write any special instructions specific to a child on the *Family Letter*, on the target word illustrations, or on the art pages.

king

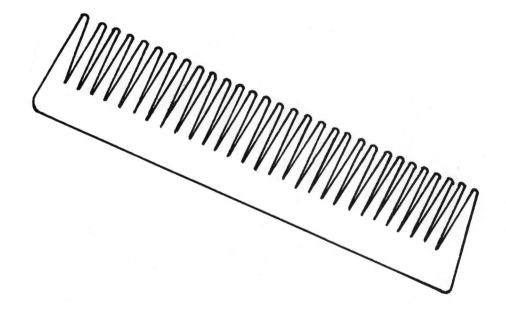

comb

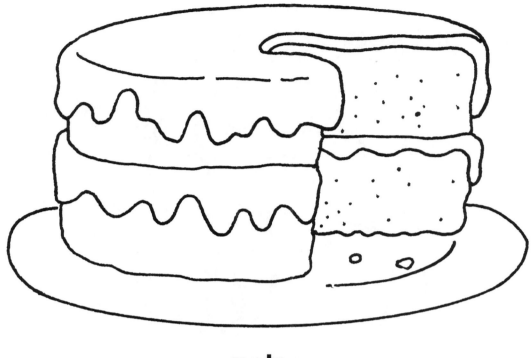

cake

cub

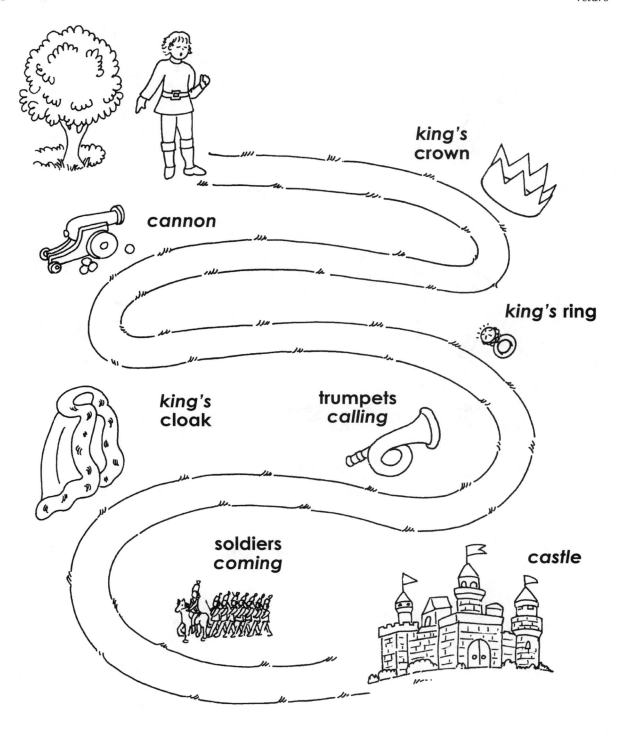

king's crown

cannon

king's ring

king's cloak

trumpets calling

soldiers coming

castle

The king is lost in the forest. Help the king get back to the castle by naming the clues along the path.

Cool Food

candy kiss

carrot

corn on the cob

cookie

candy cane

cola

cone

cocoa

Color the food. Do you like _____?

Family Letter

Date: _____

Dear Family,

In this lesson, the emphasis is on producing the *k* sound at the beginning of words. When making the *k* sound, the back part of the tongue is raised to make contact with the soft palate. It is then quickly lowered with a release of breath.

The book *I Am King,* by Mary Packard, provides good practice for the *k* sound. In this story, a little boy uses his imagination and pretends to be a mighty king in a castle who enjoys giving many commands to his army! The word *king* is a good target because of the sound sequence "k–i–ng." To make the *ing* sound in the word *king*, the back of the tongue is raised against the soft palate as when forming the *k* sound. The mouth is also completely blocked as it is when making the *k* sound. Thus the *ing* sound in the word *king* makes production of the *k* sound much easier.

Listening Lists

Read this list to your child. Slightly emphasize the *k* sound at the beginning of each word.

cannon	kite	cough	castle
crown	carry	cool	kitten
cane	color		

Target Words

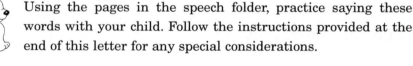

Using the pages in the speech folder, practice saying these words with your child. Follow the instructions provided at the end of this letter for any special considerations.

king	cub
comb	cake

Suggested Home Activities

1. Read the story *I Am King* to your child. Help your child say the word *king* as you review the story.

2. Talk about different foods beginning with the *k* sound (e.g., candy kisses, cola, cabbage).

3. Find and count the kings in a deck of cards. Slightly emphasize the *k* sound in the words *king* and *count*.

4. Kick a football outside. Help your child say *kick* each time it's his or her turn to kick the ball.

5. Review the *King's Castle* art page. Talk about how the pictures relate to the story *I Am King*. Help your child say the *k* sound at the beginning of the words *king* and *castle*. Name the clues along the path.

6. With the *Cool Food* art page, ask your child to point to the food he or she likes. Ask your child the name of the food as you help him or her produce the *k* sound.

Songs and Rhymes

The following song and rhyme are being practiced in class. You can help your child use the *k* sound by having him or her listen as you slightly emphasize the *k* sound at the beginning of the underlined words.

"She'll Be <u>Comin</u>' 'Round the Mountain"

She'll be <u>comin</u>' 'round the mountain when she <u>comes</u>.
She'll be <u>comin</u>' 'round the mountain when she <u>comes</u>.
She'll be <u>comin</u>' 'round the mountain,
she'll be <u>comin</u>' 'round the mountain,
she'll be <u>comin</u>' 'round the mountain when she <u>comes</u>.

"Old <u>King</u> <u>Cole</u>"

Old <u>King</u> <u>Cole</u> was a merry old soul,
and a merry old soul was he.
He <u>called</u> for his <u>cap</u> and he <u>called</u> for his <u>comb</u>,
and he <u>called</u> for his <u>candy</u> <u>canes</u> three.

Special Considerations

Sincerely,

_____

COOKIE'S WEEK

PATTERN

Velars

TARGET PHONEME

Word-initial /k/

TARGET WORDS

key, cow, caw, car

OPENING CENTER

GOAL

To introduce word-initial /k/

MATERIALS

1. One set of alphabet letters (Appendix C)

2. One brightly colored feather

3. One tongue depressor per child

4. Book titled *Cookie's Week* (1997), by Cindy Ward

Optional Materials

Bucket of objects such as a carrot, a comb, a cake, a candy cane, a candy kiss, corn, a cup, a kangaroo, a cookie

PROCEDURE

1. Introduce the letter *k* in the set of alphabet letters and demonstrate correct production of /k/. Sing the "Alphabet Song" (to the tune of "Twinkle, Twinkle, Little Star") and point to the letter *k* in the set of alphabet letters. (If appropriate, also point out that the letter *c* can sometimes make /k/.)

Helpful Hints

- *Use the tongue depressors to gently hold down the tip of a child's tongue, thus allowing the elevation of the back of the tongue when /k/ is produced.*

- *It is also effective for some children to "cough" to produce /k/, which assists in directing attention to the back part of the throat.*

Optional Activity

Have the children close their eyes and reach into the bucket for an object. Model the name of the object, articulating word-initial /k/. Have the children produce the word or word approximation after your model.

2. Have each child imitate /k/. Hold the brightly colored feather in front of your mouth and produce /k/ to demonstrate the explosive release of /k/. Hold the feather in front of each child's mouth and have him or her produce /k/. Have the children pretend they are a crow and "caw." The higher pitch helps the child associate that pitch with an elevated back of the tongue.

3. Introduce *Cookie's Week*. Point out the letter *c* and the letter *k* in the title words *Cookie's* and *week*. The word *Cookie's*, from the title, can be used as an example of how the letter *c* and letter *k* often make the same sound.

4. Read *Cookie's Week*. Model word-initial /k/ in the words *Cookie, can, kitchen*, etc.

5. Say the rhyme "Kool-Aid" and sing the song "The Farmer in the Dell."

"Kool-Aid"

Kool-aid, Kool-aid tastes great.
Kool-aid, Kool-aid can't wait.

"The Farmer in the Dell"

The farmer in the dell.
The farmer in the dell.
Hi-ho the derry-o, the farmer in the dell.

The farmer takes a cat.
The farmer takes a cat.
Hi-ho the derry-o,
the farmer takes a cat.

(Repeat with "The cat takes a carrot...," "The carrot takes the corn...," "The corn takes a king...," "The king takes a Coke....")

LISTENING CENTER

GOAL

To provide clear auditory stimuli for word-initial /k/

Optional Materials

Cookie cutters shaped like a cow, a cake, a car, or the letter k

MATERIALS

1. One amplifier and one connector with headset per child

2. Listening list: *can, keep, come, cat, cap, cup, cat, coat, cold, coal*

3. Illustrations of the four target words (pages 120–121; duplicate, cut out, and staple together)

4. Play dough

PROCEDURE

1. Instruct the children to wear their headsets and to listen. Speak into the amplifier and read the listening list to the children.

2. Introduce the four target words—*key, cow, caw, car*—to the children using the illustrations.

3. Instruct the children to continue wearing their headsets as you present a model of each target word. Have the children take turns repeating each word after it has been presented to each of them.

> **Optional Activity**
>
> *Using the play dough and the cookie cutters, help the children cut out cows, cake, cars, or the letter* k.

PRACTICE CENTER

GOAL

To facilitate production of word-initial /k/

MATERIALS

1. One printed name card per child (see page 14)

2. Illustrations of the four target words (pages 120–121; duplicate, cut out, and staple together one set per child)

3. Colored markers

4. Each child's *Remediation Data Form* (Appendix B)

5. *Family Letter* (pages 124–125; duplicate one per child)

6. One speech folder per child

> **Optional Materials**
>
> *Stickers beginning with word-initial /k/ (e.g., candy, candy cane, candy kiss, or cookie stickers)*

PROCEDURE

1. Have the children find their own name card. Once identified, instruct the children to finger-trace and say the letters in their names.

2. Instruct the children to color the four target word illustrations—*key, cow, caw, car*—using the colored markers.

3. Have the children take turns naming the target word illustrations. The goal is to elicit word-initial /k/.

> **Optional Activity**
>
> *Have the children choose a sticker to put on their folders. Then talk or ask questions about the sticker to elicit word-initial /k/ productions (e.g., "What kind of sticker did you choose?" to elicit "I chose a candy cane").*

4. Document the children's productions on their *Remediation Data Forms.*

5. Write notes related to each child's goal on his or her *Family Letter*.

ART CENTER

GOAL

To provide additional word-initial /k/ production practice and to create visual aids for home activities

MATERIALS

1. *Cookies!* (page 122; duplicate one per child)

2. Crayons

3. *Calico Cat* (page 123; duplicate one per child)

4. Glue

5. Cotton balls in a variety of colors

PROCEDURE

Cookies!

1. Give the children crayons and tell them to color the cookies.

2. Model and elicit word-initial /k/ in the words *color* and *cookie.*

3. Help the children count the cookies. While counting, ask the children "What are we doing?" to elicit "Counting cookies."

4. Send this art page home in the child's speech folder.

Calico Cat

1. Instruct the children to glue different colored cotton balls onto the cat to make a calico cat.

2. Talk about the different colored cotton balls on the calico cat. Model and elicit word-initial /k/ in the words *colored, cotton, calico,* and *cat.*

3. Allow the art page to dry, and then send it home in the child's speech folder the following session.

HOME PRACTICE

GOAL

To provide home suggestions for what the children can do in the context of their everyday lives

MATERIALS

1. Each child's set of colored target word illustrations

2. Each child's completed art pages

3. Each child's speech folder

4. Each child's *Family Letter*

PROCEDURE

1. Collect the children's colored target word illustrations and completed art pages, and send them home in their speech folders.

2. Write any special instructions specific to a child on the *Family Letter*, on the target word illustrations, or on the art pages.

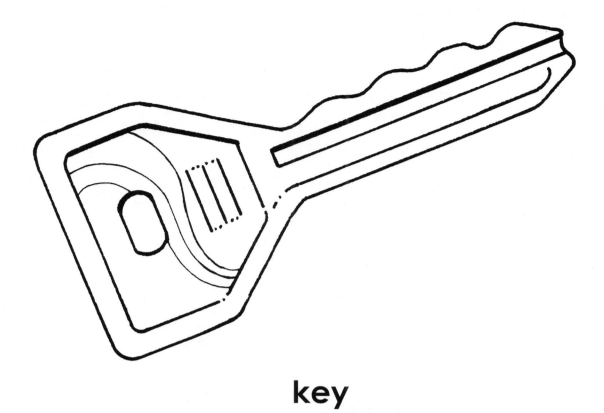

key

cow

Kenny Crow says, "Caw."

car

Color and count the cookies.

Glue colored cotton balls on the calico cat. Talk about the different colored cotton balls on the calico cat.

Family Letter

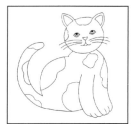

Date: _____

Dear Family,

In this lesson, the focus is on producing the *k* sound at the beginning of words. To produce the *k* sound, the back part of the tongue is raised and makes contact with the soft palate. It's then lowered with a quick release of breath.

The book for this lesson is *Cookie's Week,* by Cindy Ward. This is a delightful story about a cat named Cookie and her escapades during a week. Children love the curiosity of Cookie and all the trouble she creates. Children who need practice making the *k* sound will benefit from hearing the words in the story such as *Cookie*, *kitchen*, *curtains*, and *cat*.

Listening List

Read this list to your child. Emphasize the *k* sound at the beginning of each word.

cat	cap	cup	cut
coat	cold	coal	can
keep	come		

Target Words

Using the pages in the speech folder, practice saying these words with your child. Follow the instructions provided at the end of this letter for any special considerations.

key	caw
cow	car

Suggested Home Activities

1. Read the story *Cookie's Week* to your child. Slightly emphasize the *k* sound when it occurs in words (e.g., *Cookie, kitchen, curtains*).

2. Bake cookies together. Count the cookies. Slightly emphasize the *k* sound in the words *count, cookie,* and *cookies*.

3. While driving in the car, talk about different colors of cars you see. Have your child ask, "What color is the car?"

4. Help your child turn the key in the lock. Slightly emphasize the word *key*.

5. Review the *Cookies!* art page. Help your child count the *cookies*.

6. Admire the *Calico Cat* art page. Talk about the different colored cotton balls. Slightly emphasize the *k* sound in *calico, cat, cotton,* and *colored*.

Rhymes and Songs

The following rhyme and song are being practiced in class. You can help your child use the *k* sound by having him or her listen as you slightly emphasize the *k* in the underlined words.

"Kool-Aid"

<u>Kool-aid</u>, <u>Kool-aid</u> tastes great.
<u>Kool-aid</u>, <u>Kool-aid</u> can't wait.

"The Farmer in the Dell"

The farmer in the dell.
The farmer in the dell.
Hi-ho the derry-o, the farmer in the dell.

The farmer takes a <u>cat</u>.
The farmer takes a <u>cat</u>.
Hi-ho the derry-o,
the farmer takes a <u>cat</u>.

(Repeat with "The <u>cat</u> takes a <u>carrot</u>...," "The <u>carrot</u> takes the <u>corn</u>...," "The <u>corn</u> takes a <u>king</u>...," "The <u>king</u> takes a <u>Coke</u>....")

Special Considerations

Sincerely,

_____

MARVIN K. MOONEY, WILL YOU PLEASE GO NOW!

PATTERN

Velars

TARGET PHONEME

Word-initial /g/

TARGET WORDS

go, garden, gum, game

OPENING CENTER

GOAL

To introduce word-initial /g/

Optional Materials

Bucket of objects such as a golf ball, gum, a game, goggles, a gorilla, a guitar, a girl

MATERIALS

1. One set of alphabet letters (Appendix C)

2. Book titled *Marvin K. Mooney, Will You Please Go Now!* (1972), by Dr. Suess

3. One tongue depressor per child

PROCEDURE

1. Introduce the letter *g* in the set of alphabet letter and demonstrate the correct production of /g/. Sing the "Alphabet Song" (to the tune of "Twinkle, Twinkle, Little Star") and point to the letter *g* in the set of alphabet letters.

2. Model a production of /g/ in isolation. Elicit /g/ from the children.

3. Introduce *Marvin K. Mooney, Will You Please Go Now!* Point out the letter *g* in the title word *go*.

4. Read *Marvin K. Mooney, Will You Please Go Now!* Model word-initial /g/ as it appears in the story (e.g., *go, get, going, ga-zoom*).

5. Sing the song "Go In and Out the Window" and say the rhyme "One for the Money."

"Go In and Out the Window"

Go in and out the window.
Go in and out the window.
Go in and out the window,
as we have done before.

"One for the Money"

One for the money,
two for the show,
three to get ready,
and four to GO!

LISTENING CENTER

GOAL

To provide clear auditory stimuli for word-initial /g/

MATERIALS

1. One amplifier and one connector with headset per child

2. Listening list: *girl, goggles, garlic, garbage, guitar, goldfish, gull, guzzle, gorilla, gas*

3. Illustrations of the four target words (pages 131–132; duplicate, cut out, and staple together)

4. Play dough

PROCEDURE

1. Instruct the children to wear their headsets and to listen. Speak into the amplifier and read the listening list to the children.

2. Introduce the four target words—*go, garden, gum, game*—to the children using the illustrations.

Helpful Hint

- *Use the tongue depressors to gently hold down the tip of each child's tongue, thus allowing the elevation of the back of the tongue.*

- *It is also helpful to press up under the chin with two fingers to help elicit /g/.*

- *Another idea is to have the children growl like a bear to facilitate /g/.*

Optional Activity

Have the children close their eyes and reach into the bucket for an object. Model the name of the object, articulating word-initial /g/. Have the children produce the word or word approximation after your model.

Optional Materials

Cookie cutters shaped like the letter g

Optional Activity

Using the play dough and the cookie cutters, help the children make the letter g. *Elicit /g/.*

3. Instruct the children to continue wearing their headsets as you present a model of each target word. Have the children take turns repeating each word after it has been presented to each of them.

4. Have the children roll a small ball using the play dough. Tell the children they are going to have a play dough race. Have them stand at one end of the table and place their play dough balls at the edge. Start the race by saying, "Ready, set, and ___." Have the children say the word *go*. Then roll the play dough balls across the table. The first ball to reach the end of the table wins.

PRACTICE CENTER

GOAL

To facilitate production of word-initial /g/

Optional Materials

Stickers beginning with /g/ (e.g., gum, goldfish, or gorilla stickers)

MATERIALS

1. One printed name card per child (see page 14)

2. Illustrations of the four target words (pages 131–132; duplicate, cut out, and staple together one set per child)

3. Colored markers

4. Each child's *Remediation Data Form* (Appendix B)

5. *Family Letter* (pages 135–136; duplicate one per child)

6. One speech folder per child

Optional Activity

Have the children choose a sticker to put on their folders. Then use a cloze procedure to elicit word-initial /g/ production (e.g., "You chose a sticker of some yummy bubble ___" to elicit "gum").

PROCEDURE

1. Have the children find their own name card. Once identified, instruct the children to finger-trace and say the letters in their names.

2. Instruct the children to color the four target word illustrations—*go, garden, gum, game*—using the colored markers.

3. Have the children take turns naming the target word illustrations. The goal is to elicit word-initial /g/.

4. Document the children's productions on their *Remediation Data Forms*.

5. Write notes related to each child's goal on his or her *Family Letter*.

ART CENTER

GOAL

To provide additional word-initial /g/ production practice and to create visual aids for home activities

MATERIALS

1. *Ready, Set, Go!* (page 133; duplicate one per child)

2. Crayons

3. *Go to the Garden* (page 134; duplicate one per child)

4. Colored pencils

PROCEDURE

> **Optional Activity**
>
> *Play a racing game to practice saying "Ready, set, go!" if time permits.*

Ready, Set, Go!

1. Talk about all the activities people can do using the word *go*. Model the word *go* in each picture.

2. Tell the children to use the crayons to color the pictures of the children "going."

3. Ask the children if they ever *go* skating, *go* running, *go* biking, etc.

4. Elicit word-initial /g/ in the word *go*.

5. Send this art page home in each child's speech folder.

Go to the Garden

1. Model word-initial /g/ in the words *go* and *garden* as you say, "Let's go to the garden."

2. Have the children find the girl. Model and elicit word-initial /g/ in *girl*. Ask the children to use the colored pencils to color the girl. Have the children find the goat and do the same. Continue with all word-initial /g/ pictures.

3. Send this art page home in each child's speech folder.

Optional Snack Activity

At the end of the session, set out a treat beginning with /g/ (e.g., goldfish [crackers], [Gummy] bears, or gum). Have each child request a snack using a production based on his or her skill level.

HOME PRACTICE

GOAL

To provide home suggestions for what the children can do in the context of their everyday lives

MATERIALS

1. Each child's set of colored target word illustrations

2. Each child's completed art pages

3. Each child's speech folder

4. Each child's *Family Letter*

PROCEDURE

1. Collect the children's colored target word illustrations and completed art pages, and then send them home in their speech folders.

2. Write any special instructions specific to a child on the *Family Letter*, on the target word illustrations, or on the art pages.

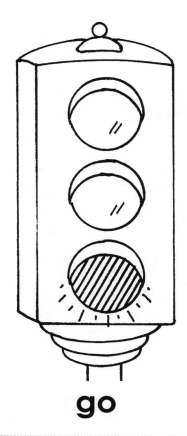

go

garden

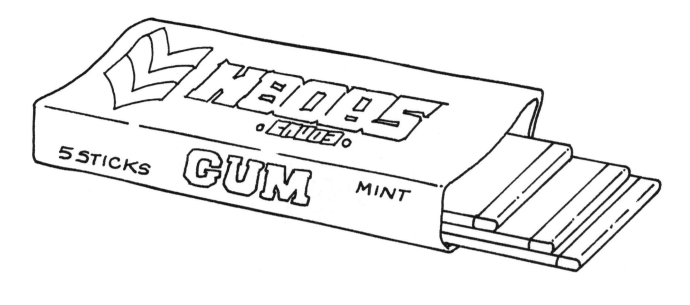

gum

game

Ready, Set, Go!

Go skating.

Go sledding.

Go running.

Go swimming.

Go biking.

Go skiing.

Go to the Garden

gate

grass

gardener

goat

glass

grapes

girl

garden

goose

Talk about each picture
that starts with "g." Then color it.

Family Letter

Date: _____

Dear Family,

In this lesson, the focus is on the *g* sound at the beginning of words. To say the *g* sound, the back part of the tongue is raised to the soft palate and then lowered with a quick release of breath. The larynx also adds voice to the sound.

We will be reading the book *Marvin K. Mooney, Will You Please Go Now!* by Dr. Suess, to introduce the *g* sound. This classic book for children uses the word *go* 30 times in a fun and humorous way. In addition to providing wonderful practice for *g* at the beginning of the word *go*, the delightful rhyming and use of repetition help to facilitate early reading skills.

Listening List

Read this list to your child. Slightly emphasize the *g* sound at the beginning of each word.

gas	girl	goggles	garlic
garbage	guitar	goldfish	gull
guzzle	gorilla		

Target Words

Using the pages in the speech folder, practice saying these words with your child. Follow the instructions provided at the end of this letter for any special considerations.

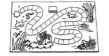

go	gum
garden	game

Suggested Home Activities

1. Read the story *Marvin K. Mooney, Will You Please Go Now!* to your child. Slightly emphasize words beginning with the *g* sound (e.g., *go, get, going, gazoom.*)

2. Play the game "Go Fish" or "Duck, Duck, Goose." Help your child say the *g* sound in *go* and *goose*.

3. Start games by saying "Ready, set, go." Have a Gummy Bear treat when you are done.

4. Go for a drive and talk about all the "stop and go" lights along the way.

5. Read the book *Go, Dog, Go,* by Dr. Seuss. Help your child say the word *go* when it occurs.

6. Review the *Ready, Set, Go!* art page with your child. Talk about activities people can do that *go.* Help your child say *go* for each of the pictures.

7. Review the *Go to the Garden* art page with your child. Have your child point to the different pictures beginning with the *g* sound, such as *girl* and *goat,* as you say them. Then help your child repeat the words.

Songs and Rhymes

The following song and rhyme are being practiced in class. You can help your child use the *g* sound by having him or her listen as you slightly emphasize the *g* sound at the beginning of the underlined words.

"<u>Go</u> In and Out the Window"

<u>Go</u> in and out the window.
<u>Go</u> in and out the window.
<u>Go</u> in and out the window,
as we have done before.

"One for the Money"

One for the money,
two for the show,
three to <u>get</u> ready,
and four to <u>GO</u>!

Special Considerations

Sincerely,

_____

HOP ON POP

PATTERN

Glottals

TARGET PHONEME

Word-initial /h/

TARGET WORDS

hat, hop, hi, house

OPENING CENTER

GOAL

To introduce word-initial /h/

MATERIALS

1. One set of alphabet letters (Appendix C)

2. Mirror

3. Candle and matches

4. One tongue depressor per child

5. Facial tissue or feather

6. Book titled *Hop on Pop* (1991), by Dr. Seuss

> **Optional Materials**
>
> *Bucket of objects such as a hat, a play house, a hamburger, a hot dog, a happy meal box, a horse*

PROCEDURE

1. Introduce the letter *h* in the set of alphabet letters and demonstrate correct production of /h/. Sing the "Alphabet Song" (to the tune of "Twinkle, Twinkle, Little Star") and point to the letter *h* in the set of alphabet letters.

2. Have the children produce /h/ while looking in the mirror (the mirror should fog).

3. Light the candle. Show the children that airflow is produced when blowing out the candle and when saying the /h/ sound. Allow each child to blow out the candle while saying /h/.

4. Have the children hold a facial tissue or feather in front of their mouths while producing /h/. Have the children observe the facial tissue or feather move with outward airflow.

5. Introduce *Hop on Pop*. Point out the letter *h* in the title word *hop*.

6. Read *Hop on Pop*. Model word-initial /h/ as it appears in the story (e.g., *hop, house, he*).

7. Sing the song "If You're Happy and You Know It," and say the rhyme "Humpty Dumpty."

"If You're Happy and You Know It"

If you're happy and you know it, clap your hands *(clap, clap)*.
If you're happy and you know it, clap your hands *(clap, clap)*.
If you're happy and you know it, then your face will surely show it.
If you're happy and you know it, clap your hands *(clap, clap)*.
(Repeat the song with "tap your head" and "hop around.")

"Humpty Dumpty"

Humpty Dumpty sat on a wall.
Humpty Dumpty had a great fall.
All the king's horses and all the king's men
couldn't put Humpty together again.

LISTENING CENTER

GOAL

To provide clear auditory stimuli for word-initial /h/

MATERIALS

1. One amplifier and one connector with headset per child

2. Listening list: *hug, hit, hamburger, happy (meal), help, hill, he, hair, hand, her*

3. Illustrations of the four target words (pages 142–143; duplicate, cut out, and staple together)

4. Play dough

5. One plastic knife per child

PROCEDURE

1. Instruct the children to wear their headsets and to listen. Speak into the amplifier and read the listening list to the children.

2. Introduce the four target words—*hat, hop, hi, house*—to the children using the illustrations.

3. Instruct the children to continue wearing their headsets as you present a model of each target word. Have the children take turns repeating each word after it has been presented to each of them.

4. Have the children roll five small balls from play dough. Elicit /hɑ/, /hæ/, /hi/, /heɪ/, /hoʊ/, /hu/ from the children. After each production, have the children flatten their play dough balls to make a "cookie."

5. Give each child play dough to roll into a six-inch snake. Have the children use the plastic knife to cut each snake into one long piece and two short pieces. Then have them form the letter *h* with the pieces. Have each child say /h/ into the amplifier while tracing the letter *h*.

PRACTICE CENTER

GOAL

To facilitate production of word-initial /h/

MATERIALS

1. One printed name card per child (see page 14)

2. Illustrations of the four target words (pages 142–143; duplicate, cut out, and staple together one set per child)

3. Colored markers

4. Each child's *Remediation Data Form* (Appendix B)

5. *Family Letter* (pages 146–147; duplicate one per child)

6. One speech folder per child

> **Optional Materials**
>
> *Stickers beginning with /h/ (e.g., hat, horse, or donkey for "he-haw" stickers)*

PROCEDURE

1. Have the children find their own name card. Once identified, instruct the children to finger-trace and say the letters in their names.

2. Instruct the children to color the four target word illustrations—*hat, hop, hi, house*—using the colored markers.

3. Have the children take turns naming the target word illustrations. The goal is to elicit word-initial /h/.

4. Document the children's productions on their *Remediation Data Forms*.

5. Write notes related to each child's goal on his or her *Family Letter*.

ART CENTER

GOAL

To provide additional word-initial /h/ production practice and to create visual aids for home activities

MATERIALS

1. *Happy Handprint* (page 144; duplicate one per child)

2. Colored markers

3. *Feelings* (page 145; duplicate one per child)

4. Crayons

PROCEDURE

Happy Handprint

1. Trace each child's hand on the *Happy Handprint* art page.

2. Write a vowel on each finger. Have each child repeat the letter name of each vowel after your model.

3. Write the letter *h* at the bottom of the hand.

4. Draw arrows from the *h* to the vowels as you say and blend /h/ with the vowel sound (the vowel sounds are long). Have the children individually repeat this production.

5. Send this art page home in the child's speech folder.

Feelings

1. Tell the children to point to the picture that shows a "hungry" child. Identify the letter *h* in the word *hungry*. Model /h/ and ask the children to imitate it. Then tell the children to color the picture.

2. Ask the children to point to the picture showing a "happy" child. Have the children imitate the word and then color the picture. Proceed to another feelings picture.

3. Send this art page home in the child's speech folder.

HOME PRACTICE

GOAL

To provide home suggestions for what the children can do in the context of their everyday lives

MATERIALS

1. Each child's set of colored target word illustrations

2. Each child's completed art pages

3. Each child's speech folder

4. Each child's *Family Letter*

PROCEDURE

1. Collect the children's colored target word illustrations and completed art pages, and send them home in their speech folders.

2. Write any special instructions specific to a child on the *Family Letter*, on the target word illustrations, or on the art pages.

Optional Snack Activity

At the end of the session, set out Hot Tamales, Ho-Ho treats, Hi-Ho crackers, or Red Hots. Have each child request a snack with productions based on his or her skill level.

hat

hop

Hi!

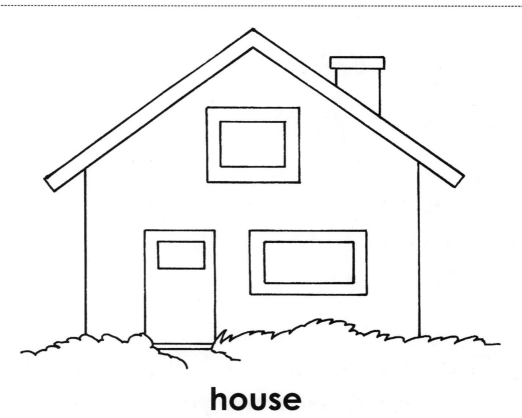

house

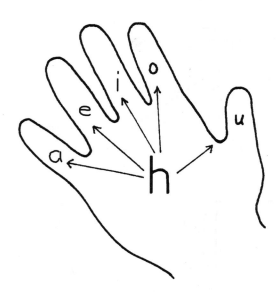

Say "ha, he, hi, ho, hu" while you touch each finger on your hand.

I'm hungry.

I'm helping.

I'm happy.

I'm hot.

I'm hurt.

I'm hiding.

Describe the feeling or action.

Family Letter

Date: _____

Dear Family,

The *h* at the beginning of words will be targeted in this lesson using words from the story *Hop on Pop*. This Dr. Seuss book is one of his simplest books, and it provides many opportunities for hearing and using the *h* sound. The *h* sound at the beginning of words is one of the earliest speech sounds children typically develop. The *h* sound is produced by breath from a continuous stream of air.

Listening List

Read this list to your child. Slightly emphasize the *h* sound at the beginning of each word.

hug	hit	hamburger	happy (meal)
help	hill	he	hair
hand	her		

Target Words

Using the pages in the speech folder, practice saying these words with your child. Follow the instructions provided at the end of this letter for any special considerations.

hat	hi
hop	house

Suggested Home Activities

1. Read the story *Hop on Pop* to your child. Have your child listen to the continuous stream of air produced by *h* at the beginning of words (e.g., *hat, house, hop*).

2. Have your child hug different family members and stuffed animals before bed. Help your child say "Hug teddy" or "I love to hug teddy."

3. Trace all family members' hands. Talk about big hands, little hands, etc.

4. Comb and brush your hair, a doll's hair, etc. Model the word *hair*.

5. Review the *Happy Handprint* art page. Practice the *h* sound in front of the vowels, *a, e, i, o,* and *u*. Review the *Feelings* art page and talk about feeling happy.

Songs and Rhymes

The following song and rhyme are being practiced in class. You can help your child use the /h/ sound by having him or her listen as you slightly emphasize the *h* sound at the beginning of the underlined words.

"If You're <u>Happy</u> and You Know It"

If you're <u>happy</u> and you know it, clap your <u>hands</u> *(clap, clap)*.
If you're <u>happy</u> and you know it, clap your <u>hands</u> *(clap, clap)*.
If you're <u>happy</u> and you know it, then your face will surely show it.
If you're <u>happy</u> and you know it, clap your <u>hands</u> *(clap, clap)*.
(Repeat the song with "tap your <u>head</u>" and" <u>hop</u> around.")

"<u>Humpty</u> Dumpty"

<u>Humpty</u> Dumpty sat on a wall.
<u>Humpty</u> Dumpty <u>had</u> a great fall.
All the king's <u>horses</u> and all the king's men
couldn't put <u>Humpty</u> together again.

Special Considerations

Sincerely,

_____

TEDDY BEAR, TEDDY BEAR

PATTERN

Alveolars

TARGET PHONEME

Word-initial /t/

TARGET WORDS

tea, two, tie, toe

OPENING CENTER

GOAL

To introduce word-initial /t/

Optional Materials

Bucket of objects such as tape, a plastic numeral 2, a top, a tail, a tiger, a toad, a teddy, a tub, toothpaste, a turtle, a ticket

MATERIALS

1. One set of alphabet letters (Appendix C)

2. Mirror

3. Book titled *Teddy Bear, Teddy Bear* (1993), by Michael Hague

4. One tongue depressor per child

PROCEDURE

1. Introduce the letter *t* in the set of alphabet letters and demonstrate correct production of /t/. Sing the "Alphabet Song" (to the tune of "Twinkle, Twinkle, Little Star") and point to the letter *t* in the set of alphabet letters.

2. Model production of /t/. Ask each child to produce /t/ in isolation.

3. Introduce *Teddy Bear, Teddy Bear.* Point out the letter *t* in the title word *Teddy*.

148

4. Read *Teddy Bear, Teddy Bear.* Model word-initial /t/ in the words *Teddy, turn, touch*, etc.

5. Say the fingerplays "Teddy Bear, Teddy Bear, Turn Around" and "Do Your Ears Hang Low?"

"Teddy Bear, Teddy Bear, Turn Around"

Teddy Bear, Teddy Bear, turn around. *(Spin around.)*
Teddy Bear, Teddy Bear, touch the ground. *(Touch the ground with your hands.)*
Teddy Bear, Teddy Bear, tap your shoe. *(Tap your toe on the ground.)*
Teddy Bear, Teddy Bear, that will do.

"Do Your Ears Hang Low?"

Do your ears hang low?
(Pull on your ears.)
Do they wobble to and fro?
(Shake your ears.)
Can you tie them in a knot?
(Pretend to tie a knot.)
Can you tie them in a bow?
(Pretend to tie a bow.)
Can you throw them over your shoulder like a continental shoulder?
(Pretend to throw them over your shoulder.)
Do your ears hang low?
(Pull on your ears.)

LISTENING CENTER

GOAL

To provide clear auditory stimuli for word-initial /t/

MATERIALS

1. One amplifier and one connector with headset per child

2. Listening list: *tickle, top, team, teach, toy, turn, touch, tell, teddy, tall*

3. Illustrations of the four target words (pages 153–154; duplicate, cut out, and staple together)

4. Play dough

5. One plastic knife per child

Optional Activity

Using the play dough and the cookie cutters, help the children cut out teddy bears or the numerals 2 and 10. Elicit /t/.

PROCEDURE

1. Instruct the children to wear their headsets and to listen. Speak into the amplifier and read the listening list to the children.

2. Introduce the four target words—*tea, two, tie, toe*—to the children using the illustrations.

3. Instruct the children to continue wearing their headsets as you present a model of each target word. Have the children take turns repeating each word after it has been presented to each of them.

4. Demonstrate for the children how to roll the play dough into a snake. Then help the children use the plastic knives to cut the snakes into two strips and make the letter *t*. Model and elicit /t/.

5. Make 10 balls of play dough and count the balls modeling word-initial /t/ in the words *two* and *ten*.

6. Make little tea cups out of the play dough. Pretend to pour, stir, and drink the tea. Elicit /t/ from each child.

PRACTICE CENTER

GOAL

To facilitate production of word-initial /t/

Optional Materials

Stickers beginning with /t/ (e.g., animals with "tails" or teddy bear stickers)

MATERIALS

1. One printed name card per child (see page 14)

2. Illustrations of the four target words (pages 153–154; duplicate, cut out, and staple together one set per child)

3. Colored markers

4. Each child's *Remediation Data Form* (Appendix B)

5. *Family Letter* (pages 157–158; duplicate one per child)

6. One speech folder per child

PROCEDURE

1. Have the children find their own name card. Once identified, instruct the children to finger-trace and say the letters in their names.

2. Have the children color the four target word illustrations—*tea, two, tie, toe*—using the colored markers.

3. Have the children take turns naming the target word illustrations. The goal is to elicit word-initial /t/.

4. Document the children's productions on their *Remediation Data Forms*.

5. Write notes related to each child's goal on his or her *Family Letter*.

ART CENTER

GOAL

To provide additional word-initial /t/ production practice and to create visual aids for home activities

MATERIALS

1. *Teddy Bear Tea Party* (page 155; duplicate one per child)

2. Soft crayons (Craypas)

3. Glue

4. Tea (dry mix)

5. *Ten Teddy Grahams* (page 156; duplicate one per child)

6. Plastic colored one-inch bears, Teddy Grahams, or any other small objects to place on drawn teddy bears

7. Brown watercolor paint

PROCEDURE

Teddy Bear Tea Party

1. Have the children color the picture using the soft crayons.

2. Place a little glue on the tea cups on the page. Help the children sprinkle tea on the glue in the tea cups. Have the children smell the tea.

3. Ask the children, "What are the bears drinking?" to elicit the word *tea*. Or ask the child "What are the bears doing?" to elicit "Having a teddy bear tea party!"

4. Allow the art page to dry, and then send it home in the child's speech folder the following session.

> **Optional Activity**
>
> *Have the children choose a sticker to put on their folders. Then talk or ask questions about the sticker to elicit word-initial /t/ productions (e.g., What kind of bear sticker did you choose?" to elicit "A teddy bear").*

Ten Teddy Grahams

1. Help the children place plastic teddy bears, Teddy Grahams, or other small objects on the drawn teddy bears.

2. Help the children count to 10, eliciting word-initial /t/ in the words *two* and *ten*.

3. Remove the objects and paint the teddy bears with brown watercolor paint.

4. Allow the art page to dry, and then send it home in the child's speech folder the following session.

Optional Snack Activity

At the end of the session, set out Teddy Graham cookies. Have each child request a snack using a production based on his or her individual skill level.

HOME PRACTICE

GOAL

To provide home suggestions for what the children can do in the context of their everyday lives

MATERIALS

1. Each child's set of colored target word illustrations

2. Each child's completed art pages

3. Each child's speech folder

4. Each child's *Family Letter*

PROCEDURE

1. Collect the children's colored target word illustrations and completed art pages, and send them home in their speech folders.

2. Write any special instructions specific to a child on the *Family Letter*, on the target word illustrations, or on the art pages.

tea

two

tie

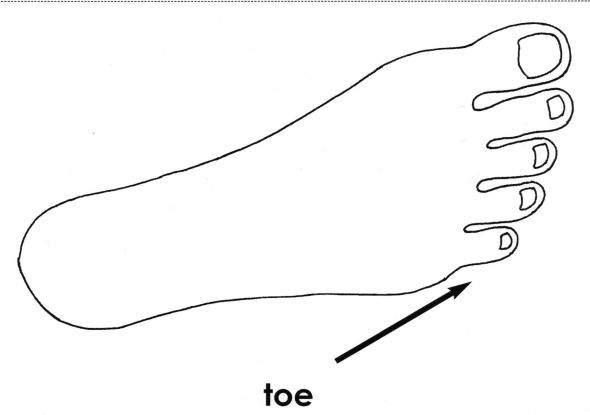

toe

Color the teddy bear picture.
What are the teddy bears drinking?

Ten Teddy Grahams

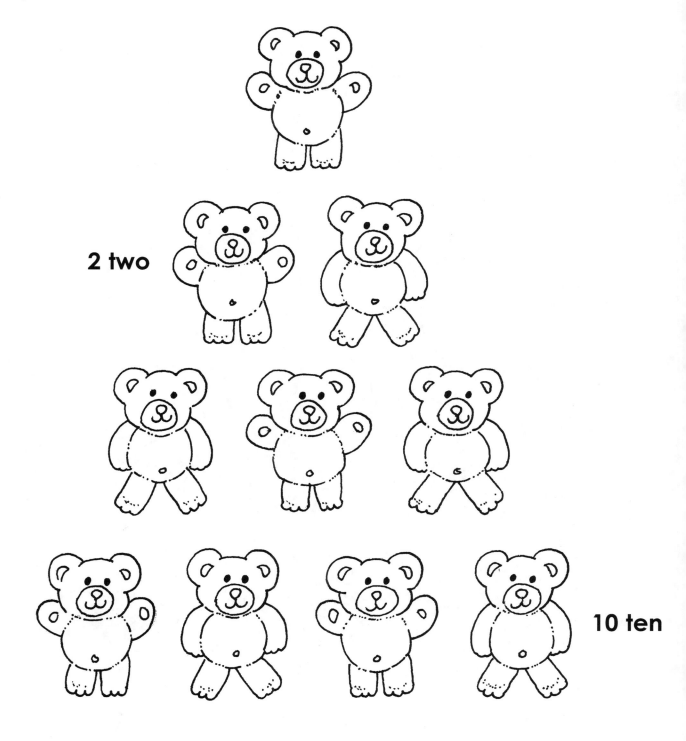

2 two

10 ten

Put a marker on each teddy bear.
How many teddy bears are there?

Family Letter

Date: _____

Dear Family,

This lesson focuses on producing the "tongue tip" sound *t*. The *t* sound is made by lightly placing the tip of the tongue at the bumpy (alveolar) ridge behind the upper front teeth. The sides of the tongue are against the side teeth. Then the tongue is dropped suddenly and the breath escapes with a sharp, explosive sound.

The book *Teddy Bear, Teddy Bear*, by Michael Hague, will be used to introduce the *t* sound. Children enjoy the magical pictures in this book. They also have fun acting out this classic childhood rhyme. This rhyme offers practice for words beginning with *t*, including *teddy, turn,* and *touch*.

Listening List

Read this list to your child. Slightly emphasize the *t* sound at the beginning of each word.

tickle	top	team	teach
toy	turn	touch	tell
teddy	tall		

Target Words

Using the pages in the speech folder, practice saying these words with your child. Follow the instructions provided at the end of this letter for any special considerations.

two	toe
tie	tea

Suggested Home Activities

1. Read the story *Teddy Bear, Teddy Bear* to your child. Slightly emphasize the *t* sound at the beginning of the words *teddy, turn,* and *touch*.

2. Have a tea party with teddy bears. Slightly emphasize the words *tea* and *teddy*.

3. Enjoy a treat together of Teddy Graham cookies. Help your child say the word *teddy*.

4. Count to 10. Slightly emphasize the *t* in *two* and *ten*.

5. Play with a toy car. Tow the car to the garage. Take the car to the car wash. Wash the tires on the car. Take turns with the car. Model the *t* at the beginning of the words *toy, tow, take, tire,* and *turn*.

6. Review the *Teddy Bear Tea Party* art page with your child. Ask your child "What are the teddy bears drinking?" Help your child respond with the word *tea*. Ask your child, "What are the bears doing?" Help your child respond, "Having a teddy bear tea party!"

7. Review the *Ten Teddy Grahams* art page with your child. Help your child count the 10 bears, and then say the words *two* and *ten*.

Songs

The following songs are being practiced in class. You can help your child use the *t* sound by having him or her listen as you slightly emphasize the *t* sound at the beginning of the underlined words.

"<u>Teddy</u> Bear, <u>Teddy</u> Bear, <u>Turn</u> Around"

<u>Teddy</u> Bear, <u>Teddy</u> Bear, <u>turn</u> around. *(Spin around.)*
<u>Teddy</u> Bear, <u>Teddy</u> Bear, <u>touch</u> the ground. *(Touch the ground with your hands.)*
<u>Teddy</u> Bear, <u>Teddy</u> Bear, <u>tap</u> your shoe. *(Tap your toe on the ground.)*
<u>Teddy</u> Bear, <u>Teddy</u> Bear, that will do.

"Do Your Ears Hang Low?"

Do your ears hang low?
(Pull on your ears.)
Do they wobble <u>to</u> and fro?
(Shake your ears.)
Can you <u>tie</u> them in a knot?
(Pretend to tie a knot.)
Can you <u>tie</u> them in a bow?
(Pretend to tie a bow.)
Can you throw them over your shoulder like a continental shoulder?
(Pretend to throw them over your shoulder.)
Do your ears hang low?
(Pull on your ears.)

Special Considerations

Sincerely,

_____

PRIMARY TARGET
PATTERNS: /s/ CLUSTERS

DRAW ME A STAR

PATTERN

/s/ clusters

TARGET CLUSTER

Word-initial /st/

TARGET WORDS

star, store, stir, stamp

OPENING CENTER

GOAL

To introduce word-initial /st/

MATERIALS

1. One set of alphabet letters (Appendix C)

2. Book titled *Draw Me a Star* (1992), by Eric Carle

3. One paper stop sign

4. A toy vehicle

5. One straw per child and one per clinician

6. Mirror

> **Optional Materials**
>
> *Bucket of objects such as a star, a sticker, a stamp, a stick, a storybook, a stapler, a stocking, a stone, a stool, a stove*

PROCEDURE

1. Introduce the letters *s* and *t* in the set of alphabet letters and demonstrate correct production of /s/ and /t/. Show the children how you blend /s/ and /t/

Helpful Hints

For children having difficulty producing /s/ because they lateralize the production, it is often helpful and motivating for them to hear the stream of air going through the straw when /s/ is produced. Demonstrate the "hissing" sound made when the straw is placed in front of the teeth and air is produced. Then have children imitate the same with their straws. For children who are interdentalizing /s/ production, direct them to place their tongue as though they will produce /t/ and then slide their tongues back to an /s/ position. Use the mirror to facilitate correct teeth and lip placement.

Optional Activity

Have the children close their eyes and reach into the bucket for an object. Model the name of the object, emphasizing word-initial /st/. Have the children produce the word or word approximation after your model.

together. Sing the "Alphabet Song" (to the tune of "Twinkle, Twinkle, Little Star") and point to the letters *s* and *t* in the set of alphabet letters.

2. Show the children the letter *s* and help them produce /s/. Show the children the letter *t* and help them produce /t/. Then show the children the letters *s* and *t* together and help them produce the /st/ cluster.

3. Introduce *Draw Me a Star*. Have the children take turns finger-tracing the letters *s* and *t* as you articulate /st/ in the title word *star*.

4. Read *Draw Me a Star*. Model word-initial /st/ in the word *star*.

5. Using the toy vehicle and the paper stop sign, have the children play "Stop and Go." For each child's turn, he or she should hold the stop sign. Push the vehicle toward the child. The child should hold up the stop sign and say, "Stop!" to make the vehicle stop and should put down the stop sign and say, "Go!" to make the vehicle go. Each child should continue this process until the vehicle reaches him or her.

6. Sing the songs "Twinkle, Twinkle, Little Star" and "I'm a Little Teapot."

"Twinkle, Twinkle, Little Star"

Twinkle, twinkle, little star. How I wonder what you are.
Up above the world so high, like a diamond in the sky.
Twinkle, twinkle, little star. How I wonder what you are.

"I'm a Little Teapot"

I'm a little teapot, short and stout.
(Put your hands on your hips and squat down slightly.)
Here is my handle,
(Keep one hand on your hip for the word handle.*)*
here is my spout.
(Raise your other hand in the air for the word spout.*)*
When I get all steamed up, hear me shout.
(Produce /s/ for steam.)
Just tip me over and pour me out.
(Tip to the side of the spout, pretending to pour tea out of it.)

LISTENING CENTER

GOAL

To provide clear auditory stimuli for word-initial /st/

MATERIALS

1. One amplifier and one connector with headset per child

2. Listening list: *stem, steam, stop, stick, steak, story, stand, sticker, steal*

3. Illustrations of the four target words (pages 166–167; duplicate, cut out, and staple together)

4. Play dough

5. Two small sticks per child (approximately 1" long)

Optional Materials

Cookie cutters shaped like stars

PROCEDURE

1. Instruct the children to wear their headsets and to listen. Speak into the amplifier and read the listening list to the children.

2. Introduce the four target words—*star, store, stir, stamp*—to the children using the illustrations.

3. Instruct the children to continue wearing their headsets as you present a model of each target word. Have the children take turns repeating each word after it has been presented to each of them.

4. Help each child make a snow person from the play dough. Then put the small sticks in the play dough to form the snow person's arms. Elicit the word *stick* from each child.

Optional Activity

Using the play dough and cookie cutters, help the children make star cookies. Elicit /st/ or the word star *from each child, as appropriate.*

PRACTICE CENTER

GOAL

To facilitate production of word-initial /st/

MATERIALS

1. One printed name card per child (see page 14)

2. Illustrations of the four target words (pages 166–167; duplicate, cut out, and staple together one set per child)

3. Colored markers

4. Each child's *Remediation Data Form* (Appendix B)

5. *Family Letter* (pages 170–171; duplicate one per child)

6. One speech folder per child

Optional Materials

Star stickers or stamps

Optional Activity

Have the children choose a star-shaped sticker or stamp to put on their folders. Then talk or ask questions about the sticker or stamp to model and elicit word-initial /st/ productions (e.g., "What shape is your sticker?" to elicit "It's a star").

PROCEDURE

1. Have the children find their own name card. Once identified, instruct the children to finger-trace and say the letters in their names.

2. Instruct the children to color the four target word illustrations—*star, store, stir, stamp*—using the colored markers.

3. Have the children take turns naming the target word illustrations. The goal is to elicit word-initial /st/.

4. Document the children's productions on their *Remediation Data Forms.*

5. Write notes related to each child's goal on his or her *Family Letter.*

ART CENTER

GOAL

To provide additional word-initial /st/ production practice and to create visual aids for home activities

MATERIALS

1. *Starry Night* (page 168; duplicate one per child)

2. Glue

3. Silver glitter

4. *Stamp the Letter* (page 169; duplicate one per child)

5. A rubber stamp, stamp marker, or six sweepstakes stamps per child

6. Ink pad (if using rubber stamps)

PROCEDURE

Starry Night

1. Have the children outline the stars with glue.

2. Help the children sprinkle the glitter on the glue. Model word-initial /st/ in the word *star.*

3. Elicit the word *star* from each child as the children sprinkle the glitter.

4. After the children have sprinkled the glitter on the stars, talk about how the glitter "twinkles." Sing "Twinkle, Twinkle, Little Star," slightly emphasizing the word *star.*

5. Have the children talk about the kinds of stars on the page (e.g., *"There's a store star," "I see a stamp star"*).

6. Allow the art page to dry, and then send it home in the child's speech folder the following session.

Stamp the Letter

1. The addresses on *Stamp the Letter* provide review for many of the books introduced in *Once Upon a Sound.* Review the addresses with the children. Then have them stamp the letters with a rubber stamp, a stamp marker, or place a sweepstakes stamp on the letter.

2. Elicit the word *stamp* from each child several times as the children stamp the letters.

3. Send this art page home in each child's speech folder.

HOME PRACTICE

GOAL

To provide home suggestions for what the children can do in the context of their everyday lives

MATERIALS

1. Each child's set of colored target word illustrations

2. Each child's completed art pages

3. Each child's speech folder

4. Each child's *Family Letter*

PROCEDURE

1. Collect the children's colored target word illustrations and completed art pages, and send them home in their speech folders.

2. Write any special instructions specific to a child on the *Family Letter*, on the target word illustrations, or on the art pages.

Optional Snack Activity

At the end of the session, set out star-shaped crackers or cookies, pretzel sticks, or Starbursts. Have each child request a snack using a production based on his or her skill level.

star

store

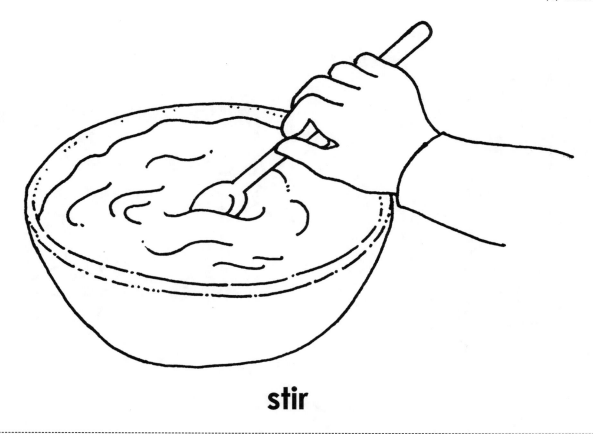

stir

stamp

Sprinkle glitter on the stars. What kinds of things do you see in the star?

Stamp the Letter

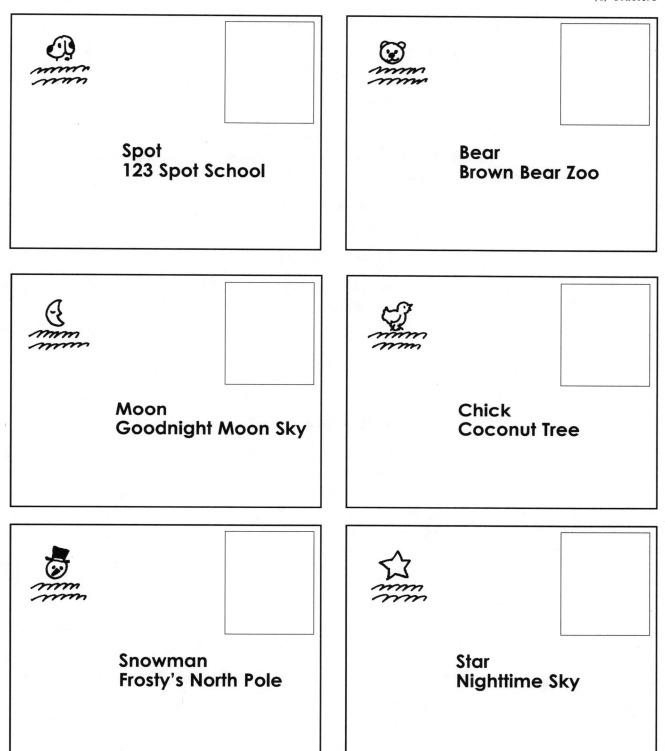

Spot
123 Spot School

Bear
Brown Bear Zoo

Moon
Goodnight Moon Sky

Chick
Coconut Tree

Snowman
Frosty's North Pole

Star
Nighttime Sky

Say stamp as you stamp the letters.

Family Letter

Date: _____

Dear Family,

In this lesson, the emphasis is on producing the *st* blend at the beginning of words. Because many children produce the *t* sound for the *s* sound, the *st* blend is often one of the easiest *s* blends to learn. Children only need to add an *s* before the *t* sound for the blend to be produced correctly. Once children have learned to produce friction with the *st* blend, it becomes easier for them to produce the *s* sound in words like *sand* and *saw*.

The book for this lesson is *Draw Me a Star,* by Eric Carle. This charming story brings out the artist in all children!

Listening List

Read this list to your child. Slightly emphasize the *st* blend at the beginning of each word.

stem	steam	stop	step
stick	steak	story	stand
sticker	steal		

Target Words

Using the pages in the speech folder, practice saying these words with your child. Follow the instructions provided at the end of this letter for any special considerations.

star	stir
store	stamp

Suggested Home Activities

1. Read the story *Draw Me A Star* to your child. Slightly emphasize the *st* blend at the beginning of the word *star*. Help your child say the word *star*.

2. Make a star and hang it in a window. Help your child say the word *star*.

3. Go shopping at a store (toy store, grocery store, etc.). Help your child say the word *store* as the two of you talk about the different stores.

4. Make Kool-aid together. Slightly emphasize the word *stir* as you stir the Kool-aid.

5. Admire your child's work on the *Starry Night* art page he or she brings home. Ask your child how he or she made the stars twinkle. Help your child say the word *star,* and talk about the kinds of stars he or she sees in the sky.

6. Talk about the *Stamp the Letter* art page your child brings home. Help your child say the *st* blend in the word *stamp* as you point to the stamp on each letter.

Songs

The following songs are being practiced in class. You can help your child use the *st* blend by having him or her listen as you slightly emphasize the *st* blend at the beginning of the underlined words.

"Twinkle, Twinkle, Little <u>Star</u>"

Twinkle, twinkle little <u>star</u>.
How I wonder what you are.
Up above the world so high,
Like a diamond in the sky.
Twinkle, twinkle little <u>star</u>.
How I wonder what you are.

"I'm a Little Teapot"

I'm a little teapot, short and <u>stout</u>.
(Put your hands on your hips and squat down slightly.)
Here is my handle,
(Keep one hand on your hip for the word handle.*)*
here is my spout.
(Raise your other hand in the air for the word spout.*)*
When I get all <u>steamed</u> up, hear me shout.
(Produce an extended s *sound for steam.)*
Just tip me over and pour me out.
(Tip to the side of the spout, pretending to pour tea out of it.)

Special Considerations

Sincerely,

FROSTY THE SNOW MAN

PATTERN

/s/ clusters

TARGET CLUSTER

Word-initial /sn/

TARGET WORDS

snake, snow, snail, snap

OPENING CENTER

GOAL

To introduce word-initial /sn/

Optional Materials

Bucket of objects such as a snowman, a snake, a snail, a snowflake, a snowball, a snack, snapshots, snow boots, a snowplow, Snoopy, a Snickers candy bar, miniature Snicker-Snacker treats, a water globe for "snow" when shook

MATERIALS

1. One set of alphabet letters (Appendix C)

2. Book titled *Frosty the Snow Man* (1950), by Annie North Bedford

3. One straw per child and one per clinician

4. Mirror

PROCEDURE

1. Introduce the letters *s* and *n* in the set of alphabet letters and demonstrate correct production of /s/ and /n/. Show the children how you blend /s/ and /n/ together. Sing the "Alphabet Song" (to the tune of "Twinkle, Twinkle, Little Star") and point to the letters *s* and *n* in the set of alphabet letters.

2. Show the children the letter *s* and help them produce /s/. Show the children the letter *n* and help them produce /n/. Then show the children the letters *s* and *n* together and help them produce the /sn/ cluster.

3. Introduce *Frosty the Snow Man.* Point out the letter *s* and the letter *n* in the title word *snow.* Have the children imitate the /sn/ blend after you model it.

4. Read *Frosty the Snow Man.* Model word-initial /sn/ in the words *snow, snow man, snow balls,* and *snow flakes.*

5. Say the fingerplays "Five Little Moneys Sneaking in a Tree" and "The Snowman Fat."

"Five Little Monkeys Sneaking in a Tree"

Five little monkeys sneaking in a tree,
teasing Mr. Alligator, "Can't catch me!"
(Hold up your five right-hand fingers and creep them upward.)
Along comes Mr. Alligator, happy as can be...
(Place both hands together and pretend to be an alligator swimming and sneaking up on the monkeys.)
Snap!
(Clasp both arms together in a loud snap.)

Repeat with
Four little monkeys... *(Do the same actions with four fingers.)*
Three little monkeys... *(Do the same actions with three fingers.)*
Two little monkeys... *(Do the same actions with two fingers.)*
One little monkey... *(Do the same actions with one finger.)*

"The Snowman Fat"

(Stand up for this fingerplay.)
The snowman fat
(Hold your arms out together to form a fat tummy.)
put on his hat
(Pretend to place a hat on your head.)
and began to dance around.
(Turn around in a circle.)
The sun came out
(Touch your hands together above your head.)
and made the snowman pout.
(Point to your mouth and pout.)
And he melted to the ground.
(Pretend to melt to the ground.)

Helpful Hints

For children having difficulty producing /s/ because they lateralize the production, it is often helpful and motivating for them to hear the stream of air going through the straw when /s/ is produced. Demonstrate the "hissing" sound made when the straw is placed in front of the teeth and air is produced. Then have children imitate the same with their straws. For children who are interdentalizing /s/ production, direct them to place their tongue as though they will produce /t/ and then slide their tongues back to an /s/ position. Use the mirror to facilitate correct teeth and lip placement.

Optional Activity

Have the children close their eyes and reach into the bucket for an object. Model the name of the object, articulating word-initial /sn/. Have the children produce the word or word approximation after your model.

173

LISTENING CENTER

GOAL

To provide clear auditory stimuli for word-initial /sn/

Optional Materials

Cookie cutters shaped like an angel or the letters s and n

MATERIALS

1. One amplifier and one connector with headset per child

2. Listening list: *snowball, snoop, snip, snore, sneak, snug, sniff, sneeze, snuggle*

3. Illustrations of the four target words (pages 177–178; duplicate, cut out, and staple together)

4. Play dough

Optional Activity

Using the play dough and cookie cutters, help the children cut out snow angels or the letters s and n. Elicit /sn/ or snow from each child, as appropriate.

PROCEDURE

1. Instruct the children to wear their headsets and to listen. Speak into the amplifier and read the listening list to the children.

2. Introduce the four target words—*snake, snow, snail, snap*—to the children using the illustrations.

3. Instruct the children to continue wearing their headsets as you present a model of each target word. Have the children take turns repeating each word after it has been presented to each of them.

4. Help the children make snowballs from the play dough. Elicit the word *snowball* from each child.

5. Use the snowballs to make snow men and snow women. Elicit the words *snow man, snow woman*, and *snow folks* from each child as they work.

PRACTICE CENTER

GOAL

To facilitate production of word-initial /sn/

MATERIALS

1. One printed name card per child (see page 14)

2. Illustrations of the four target words (pages 177–178; duplicate, cut out, and staple together one set per child)

3. Colored markers

4. Each child's *Remediation Data Form* (Appendix B)

5. *Family Letter* (pages 181–182; duplicate one per child)

6. One speech folder per child

PROCEDURE

1. Have the children find their own name card. Once identified, instruct the children to finger-trace and say the letters in their names.

2. Instruct the children to color the four target word illustrations—*snake, snow, snail, snap*—using the colored markers.

3. Have the children take turns naming the target word illustrations. The goal is to elicit word-initial /sn/.

4. Document the children's productions on their *Remediation Data Forms*.

5. Write notes related to each child's goal on his or her *Family Letter*.

ART CENTER

GOAL

To provide additional word-initial /sn/ production practice and to create visual aids for home activities

MATERIALS

1. *Snow Folks* (page 179; duplicate one per child onto blue paper)

2. Crayons

3. One cotton swab per child

4. Glue

5. Shredded coconut

6. *Snow Scene* (page 180; duplicate one per child)

7. Silver glitter pens

PROCEDURE

Snow Folks

1. Have the children use crayons to color the clothing on the snow folks. Model and elicit word-initial /sn/ in the words *snow, snow man, snow woman, snow scarf,* and *snow folks.*

2. Have the children use the cotton swabs to dot glue on the page for snow.

3. Have the children sprinkle shredded coconut onto the glue. Model and elicit word-initial /sn/ in the words *snow, snowing, snow man, snow woman,* and *snow folks.*

4. Allow the art page to dry, and then send it home in the child's speech folder the following session.

Snow Scene

1. Model word-initial /sn/ in the word *snow* as you say the name of each snow picture (e.g., "That's a snow bank").

2. Have the children use the silver glitter pens to circle each snow picture in the snow scene. Elicit the words *snow, snow bank, snowball*s, etc. from each child as the children circle each picture with the glitter pens.

3. Send the art page home in the child's speech folder.

HOME PRACTICE

<table>
<tr><td>

Optional Snack Activity

At the end of the session, set out Ginger Snap cookies or miniature Snicker-Snacker treats. Have the children request a snack using a production based on his or her skill level.

</td></tr>
</table>

GOAL

To provide home suggestions for what the children can do in the context of their everyday lives

MATERIALS

1. Each child's set of colored target word illustrations

2. Each child's completed art pages

3. Each child's speech folder

4. Each child's *Family Letter*

PROCEDURE

1. Collect the children's colored target word illustrations and completed art pages, and send them home in their speech folders.

2. Write any special instructions specific to a child on the *Family Letter*, on the target word illustrations, or on the art pages.

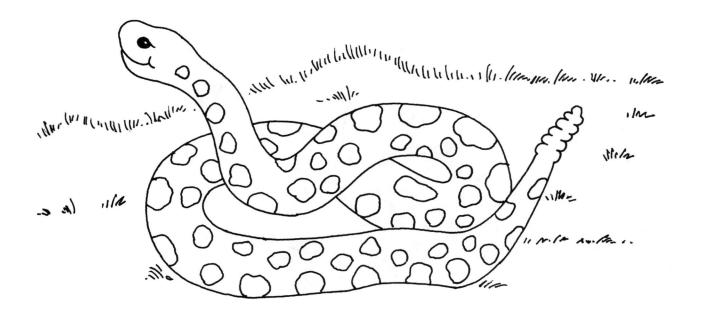

snake

snow

snail

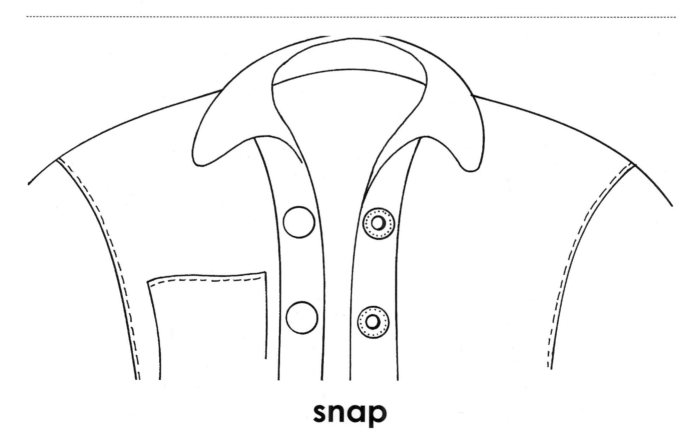

snap

Snow Folks

Sprinkle coconut snow on the snow folks.
Say "snow" as you sprinkle the coconut.

Snow Scene

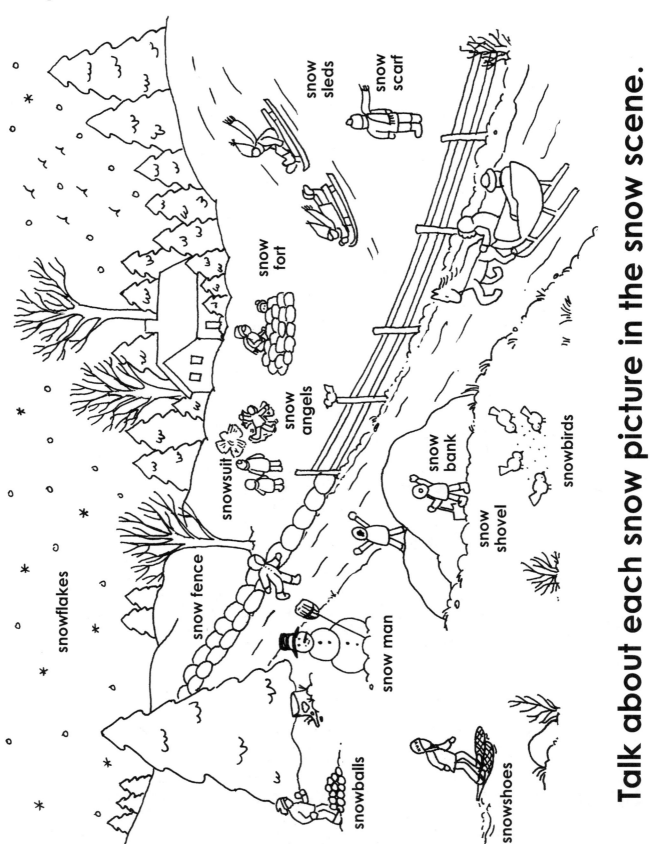

snow sleds

snow scarf

snow fort

snow angels

snowsuit

snowflakes

snow fence

snow bank

snow shovel

snowbirds

snow man

snowballs

snowshoes

Talk about each snow picture in the snow scene.

Family Letter

Date: _____

Dear Family,

In this lesson, the focus is on producing the *sn* blend at the beginning of words. The *sn* blend is produced with the continuous airflow of the *s* sound in combination with the nasal quality of the *n* sound. When producing the *sn* blend, the children learn to "smile" and make the "hissing" snake sound. This "smile" position brings the upper and lower teeth together and helps eliminate their sticking the tongue tip between the teeth (referred to as "the snake peeking out from between the teeth").

The book for this lesson is *Frosty the Snow Man*, by Annie North Bedford. This story contains many words with the *sn* blend, such as *snow, snow man,* and *snowflake*. Children listen to and say the *sn* blend in a fun and meaningful way. The warm-hearted, magical character of Frosty is one that children always enjoy.

Listening List

Read this list to your child. Slightly emphasize the *sn* blend at the beginning of each word.

snowball	snoop	snip	snore
snack	sneak	snug	sniff
sneeze	snuggle		

Target Words

Using the pages in the speech folder, practice saying these words with your child. Follow the instructions provided at the end of this letter for any special considerations.

snake	snail
snow	snap

Suggested Home Activities

1. Read the story *Frosty the Snow Man* to your child. Slightly emphasize the *sn* blend at the beginning of the words *snow, snow man,* and *snowflake*.

2. Let your child practice snapping various articles of clothing. Model the *sn* blend in the word *snap*. Help your child say the word *snap*.

3. When baking with your child, take turns sniffing ingredients with distinctive aromas (e.g., pepper, cinnamon, vanilla). Model the *sn* sound in the word *sniff* (e.g., "I will sniff the pepper"). Help your child say the word *sniff*.

4. Admire the snow on the *Snow Folks* art page. Tell your child to name the snow folks.

5. Talk about the *Snow Scene* art page. Help your child say the *sn* blend in the *snow* words.

Fingerplays

The following fingerplays are being practiced in class. You can help your child use the *sn* blend by having him or her listen as you slightly emphasize the *sn* at the beginning of the underlined words.

"Five Little Monkeys Sneaking in a Tree"

Five little monkeys <u>sneaking</u> in a tree,
teasing Mr. Alligator, "Can't catch me!"
(Hold up your five right-hand fingers and creep them upward.)
Along comes Mr. Alligator, happy as can be...
(Place both hands together and pretend to be an alligator swimming and sneaking up on the monkeys.)
<u>Snap</u>!
(Clasp both arms together in a loud snap.)

Repeat with
Four little monkeys... *(Do the same actions with four fingers.)*
Three little monkeys... *(Do the same actions with three fingers.)*
Two little monkeys... *(Do the same actions with two fingers.)*
One little monkey... *(Do the same actions with one finger.)*

"The <u>Snowman</u> Fat"

(Stand up for this fingerplay.)
The <u>snowman</u> fat
(Hold your arms out together to form a fat tummy.)
put on his hat
(Pretend to place a hat on your head.)
and began to dance around.
(Turn around in a circle.)
The sun came out
(Touch your hands together above your head.)
and made the <u>snowman</u> pout.
(Point to your mouth and pout.)
And he melted to the ground.
(Pretend to melt to the ground.)

Special Considerations

Sincerely,

_____

WHERE'S SPOT?

PATTERN

/s/ clusters

TARGET CLUSTER

Word-initial /sp/

TARGET WORDS

spider, Spot, spoon, spill

OPENING CENTER

GOAL

To introduce word-initial /sp/

MATERIALS

1. One set of alphabet letters (Appendix C)

2. Book titled *Where's Spot?* (1980), by Eric Hill

3. One straw per child and one per clinician

4. Mirror

Optional Materials

Bucket of objects such as a spoon, a spool of thread, a spider, a sponge, Spot (the dog), a can of spinach, a spinner

PROCEDURE

1. Introduce the letters *s* and *p* in the set of alphabet letters and demonstrate correct production of /s/ and /p/. Show the children how you blend /s/ and /p/ together. Sing the "Alphabet Song" (to the tune of "Twinkle, Twinkle, Little Star") and point to the letters *s* and *p* in the set of alphabet letters.

2. Show the children the letter *s* and help them produce /s/. Show the children the letter *p* and help them produce /p/. Then show the children the letters *s* and *p* together and help them produce the /sp/ cluster.

3. Introduce *Where's Spot?* Point to the letter *s* and the letter *p* in the title word *Spot.* Have the children finger-trace the *s* and the *p* as you emphasize /sp/ the title word *Spot.*

4. Read *Where's Spot?* Model word-initial /sp/ in the word *Spot* while reading the book.

5. Sing the song "The Itsy-Bitsy Spider" and say the rhyme "Hey Diddle, Diddle."

"The Itsy-Bitsy Spider"

The itsy-bitsy spider climbed up the water spout.
(Move your index fingers and thumbs in an upward chain.)
Down came the rain and washed the spider out.
(Move your fingers in a downward motion for rain.
Cross and uncross your arms quickly to "wash the spider out.")
Out came the sun and dried up all the rain.
(Make a big circle over your head with your arms for the sun.)
And the itsy-bitsy spider climbed up the spout again.
(Move your index fingers and thumbs in an upward chain.)

"Hey Diddle, Diddle"

Hey diddle, diddle, the cat and the fiddle,
the cow jumped over the moon.
The little dog laughed to see such sport,
and the dish ran away with the spoon.

LISTENING CENTER

GOAL

To provide clear auditory stimuli for word-initial /sp/

MATERIALS

1. One amplifier and connector with headset per child

2. Listening list: *spy, spin, speak, spool, spear, sponge, spell, spoke, sport, speed*

3. Illustrations of the four target words (pages 188–189; duplicate, cut out, and staple together)

4. Play dough

PROCEDURE

1. Instruct the children to wear their headsets and to listen. Speak into the amplifier and read the listening list to the children.

2. Introduce the four target words—*spider, Spot, spoon, spill*—to the children using the illustrations.

3. Instruct the children to continue wearing their headsets as you present a model of each target word. Have the children take turns repeating each word after it has been presented to each of them.

4. Help the children make spiders from the play dough. Elicit the word *spider* from each child.

PRACTICE CENTER

GOAL

To facilitate production of word-initial /sp/

MATERIALS

1. One printed name card per child (see page 14)

2. Illustrations of the four target words (pages 188–189; duplicate, cut out, and staple together one set per child)

3. Colored markers

4. Each child's *Remediation Data Form* (Appendix B)

5. *Family Letter* (pages 192–193; duplicate one per child)

6. One speech folder per child

PROCEDURE

1. Have the children find their own name card. Once identified, instruct the children to finger-trace and say the letters in their names. Tell the children they are spelling their name. Model /sp/ in the word *spelling*.

2. Instruct the children to color the four target word illustrations—*spider, Spot, spoon, spill*—using the colored markers.

3. Have the children take turns naming the target word illustrations. The goal is to elicit word-initial /sp/.

Optional Materials

Cookie cutter shaped like a dog

Optional Activity

Using the play dough and dog-shaped cookie cutter, help the children make dog cookies. Then help the children put bits of play dough on the dog for spots. Elicit /sp/ or the word spot *from each child, as appropriate.*

Optional Materials

Spider stickers

Optional Activity

Have the children choose a spider sticker to put on their folders. Then sing the song "The Itsy-Bitsy (Spider)," omitting the word spider. *Have the children fill in the word* spider *as you sing.*

4. Document the children's productions on their *Remediation Data Forms.*

5. Write notes related to each child's goal on his or her *Family Letter.*

ART CENTER

GOAL

To provide additional word-initial /sp/ production practice and to create visual aids for home activities

MATERIALS

1. *Spotty* (page 190; duplicate one per child)

2. Sponges cut in small circles

3. Tempera paint

4. *Sparkling Spider Web* (page 191; duplicate one per child)

5. Glitter glue

6. Scissors

7. Paper punch

8. Yarn cut into approximately 6" lengths; one per child

PROCEDURE

Spotty

1. Have each child dip the small, round sponge into the paint and make spots on the dog. Model word-initial /sp/ in the words *sponge, spot,* and *Spotty.*

2. Elicit the words *sponge, spot,* and *Spotty* from each child as the children paint the spots onto their dogs.

3. Allow the art page to dry, and then send it home in the child's speech folder the following session.

Sparkling Spider Web

1. Help the children outline the spider web with glitter glue. Model and elicit word-initial /sp/ in the word *spider.*

2. Point out the speckles in the glue. Elicit the word *speckles* from each child as you talk about the glue.

3. Cut out the spider and use the paper punch to punch a hole in the spider and in the web. Attach the spider to the web with the yarn.

4. Have the children move the spider onto the web. Elicit the word *spider* from each child.

5. Allow the art page to dry, and then send it and the spider home in the child's speech folder the following session.

HOME PRACTICE

GOAL

To provide home suggestions for what the children can do in the context of their everyday lives

MATERIALS

1. Each child's set of colored target word illustrations

2. Each child's completed art pages

3. Each child's speech folder

4. Each child's *Family Letter*

PROCEDURE

1. Collect the children's colored target word illustrations and completed art pages, and send them home in their speech folders.

2. Write any special instructions specific to a child on the *Family Letter*, on the target word illustrations, or on the art pages.

Optional Snack Activity

At the end of the session, set out candy sprinkles and call them speckles. Use a spoon to frost graham crackers and put the speckles on top. Have each child request a snack using a production based on his or her skill level.

spider

Spot

188

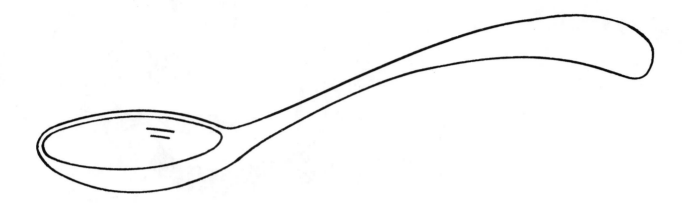

spoon

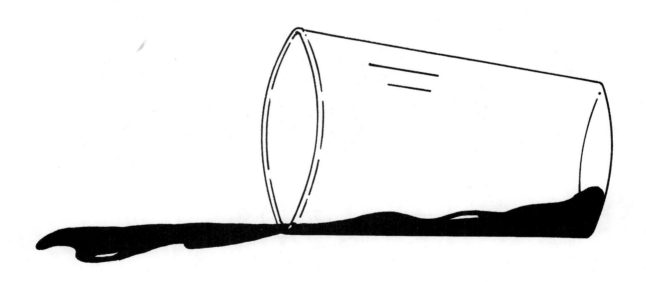

spill

Use the sponge to make spots.
Talk about how you made the spots.

Use glitter glue to help your spider spin a sparkling web. Talk about the speckles that sparkle in the spider's web.

Family Letter

Date: _____

Dear Family,

In this lesson, the *sp* blend is introduced. The *sp* blend is produced with the continuous airflow of the *s* sound combined with the explosive "pop" of the *p* sound.

The book for this lesson is *Where's Spot?* by Eric Hill. This book provides children with many opportunities to practice the *sp* blend. It is also a wonderful book for teaching concepts such as behind, inside, in, and under. Children love searching for Spot as he hides in various places.

Listening Lists

Read this list to your child. Slightly emphasize the *sp* blend at the beginning of each word.

spy	spin	speak	spool
spear	sponge	spell	spoke
sport	speed		

Target Words

Using the pages in the speech folder, practice saying these words with your child. Follow the instructions provided at the end of this letter for any special considerations.

spider	spoon
Spot	spill

Suggested Home Activities

1. Read the story *Where's Spot* to your child. Slightly emphasize the *sp* blend at the beginning of the word *spot*. Ask your child the name of the dog.

2. Play "I Spy." This is done by describing something in the room and having your child guess what it is you're describing. For example, you might say, "I spy something that is big and soft and you sleep in it. What do I spy?" Your child might respond "You spy the bed."

3. Spin in circles. Help your child say the *sp* blend in the word *spin*.

4. Set the table and have your child place a spoon, fork, and knife at each spot. Emphasize the *sp* blend in the words *spoon* and *spot*. Help your child say the words *spoon* and *spot* as he or she sets the table.

5. Admire the *Spotty* and art page your child brings home. Ask your child how the spots on Spotty were made. Model the words *spots* and *Spotty*.

6. Review the *Sparkling Spider Web* art. Talk about what lives on the sparkling web. Help your child say the words *spider* and *sparkling*.

Songs and Rhymes

The following song and rhyme are being practiced in class. You can help your child use the *sp* blend by having him or her listen as you slightly emphasize the *sp* blend at the beginning of the underlined words.

"The Itsy-Bitsy <u>Spider</u>"

The itsy-bitsy <u>spider</u> climbed up the water <u>spout</u>.
(Move your index fingers and thumbs in an upward chain.)
Down came the rain and washed the <u>spider</u> out.
(Move your fingers in a downward motion for rain.
Cross and uncross your arms quickly to "wash the spider out.")
Out came the sun and dried up all the rain.
(Make a big circle with your arms for the sun.)
And the itsy-bitsy <u>spider</u> climbed up the <u>spout</u> again.
(Move your index fingers and thumbs in an upward chain.)

"Hey Diddle, Diddle"

Hey diddle, diddle, the cat and the fiddle,
the cow jumped over the moon.
The little dog laughed to see such <u>sport</u>,
and the dish ran away with the <u>spoon</u>.

Special Considerations

Sincerely,

_____

THE SNOWY DAY

PATTERN

/s/ clusters

TARGET CLUSTER

Word-initial /sm/

TARGET WORDS

smell, smile, smoke, smash

OPENING CENTER

GOAL

To introduce word-initial /sm/

MATERIALS

Optional Materials

Bucket of objects such as aromatic or scented things to smell (e.g., spices, perfumes, laundry softeners) or things that have smiles (e.g., dolls, photos of people)

1. One set of alphabet letters (Appendix C)

2. Book titled *The Snowy Day* (1962), by Ezra Jack Keats

3. Camera (real or toy)

4. A globe or a small map of the world

5. One straw per child and one per clinician

6. Mirror

PROCEDURE

1. Introduce the letters *s* and *m* in the set of alphabet letters and demonstrate correct production of /s/ and /m/. Show the children how you blend /s/ and /m/ together. Sing the "Alphabet Song" (to the tune of "Twinkle, Twinkle, Little Star") and point to the letters *s* and *m* in the set of alphabet letters.

2. Show the children the letter *s* and help them produce /s/. Show the children the letter *m* and help them produce /m/. Then show the children the letters *s* and *m* together and help them produce the /sm/ cluster.

3. Introduce *The Snowy Day*. Draw the children's attention to the cover and ask them if a snowy day would make them smile. Discuss the things about a snowy day that might make them smile. Slightly emphasize /sm/ in the word *smile*.

4. Read *The Snowy Day*. Model /sm/ in the words *smacking* and *smiling*.

5. Using the camera, have the children take turns smiling and taking pretend pictures of each other. Tell the children to say the word *smile* before taking a picture.

6. Sing the songs "S'Mores" and "It's a Small World."

"S'Mores"
(Sing to the tune of "Here We Go Round the Mulberry Bush.")

This is the way we make our s'mores.
We make our s'mores, we make our s'mores.
This is the way we make our s'mores,
when we are at school.

(Repeat with "This is the way we eat our s'mores...")

"It's a Small World"
(Show a globe or a small map of the world while singing the song.)

It's a small world after all.
It's a small world after all.
It's a small world after all.
It's a small, small world.

LISTENING CENTER

GOAL

To provide clear auditory stimuli for word-initial /sm/

MATERIALS

1. One amplifier and one connector with headset per child

2. Listening list: *small, smooth, smear, smock, smack, smart, smog, smother, smudge, smolder*

Helpful Hints

For children having difficulty producing /s/ because they lateralize the production, it is often helpful and motivating for them to hear the stream of air going through the straw when /s/ is produced. Demonstrate the "hissing" sound made when the straw is placed in front of the teeth and air is produced. Then have children imitate the same with their straws. For children who are interdentalizing /s/ production, direct them to place their tongue as though they will produce /t/ and then slide their tongues back to an /s/ position. Use the mirror to facilitate correct teeth and lip placement.

Optional Activity

Have the children smell the various objects in the bucket. Model and elicit word-initial /sm/ when saying the word smell *(e.g., "What do you smell?" to elicit "I smell flowers").*

3. Illustrations of the four target words (pages 199–200; duplicate, cut out, and staple together)

4. Play dough

PROCEDURE

1. Instruct the children to wear their headsets and to listen. Speak into the amplifier and read the listening list to the children.

2. Introduce the four target words—*smell, smile, smoke, smash*—to the children using the illustrations.

3. Instruct the children to continue wearing their headsets as you present a model of each target word. Have the children take turns repeating each word after it has been presented to each of them.

4. Help the children make small and large objects from the play dough (e.g., smiles, balls, snakes, snow people). Elicit the word *small* from each child as he or she identifies the small item in each pair.

5. Help the children make a face from the play dough that has two eyes, one nose, and a big smile. Slightly emphasize word-initial /sm/ in the word *smile*.

PRACTICE CENTER

GOAL

To facilitate production of word-initial /sm/

MATERIALS

Optional Materials

Smiley face stickers

1. One printed name card per child (see page 14)

2. Illustrations of the four target words (pages 199–200; duplicate, cut out, and staple together one set per child)

3. Colored markers

4. Each child's *Remediation Data Form* (Appendix B)

5. *Family Letter* (pages 203–204; duplicate one per child)

6. One speech folder per child

PROCEDURE

1. Have the children find their own name card. Once identified, instruct the children to finger-trace and say the letters in their names.

2. Have the children color the four target word illustrations—*smell, smile, smoke, smash*—using the colored markers.

3. Have the children take turns naming the target word illustrations. The goal is to elicit word-initial /sm/.

4. Document the children's productions on their *Remediation Data Forms*.

5. Write notes related to each child's goal on his or her *Family Letter*.

ART CENTER

GOAL

To provide additional word-initial /sm/ production practice and to create visual aids for home activities

MATERIALS

1. *Small or Large?* (page 201; duplicate one per child)

2. One red crayon per child

3. *Smiley Faces* (page 202; duplicate one per child)

PROCEDURE

Small or Large?

1. Tell the children to look at the two objects in each row. (If necessary have them put their fingers below the two objects to help them hold their place on the page.) Tell them to use their red crayons to circle the smaller object in each row. Elicit the word *small* from each child after he or she correctly identifies the smaller object in each row.

2. Send this art page home in each child's speech folder.

Smiley Faces

1. Using a red crayon, help the children draw smiles on the faces. Model word-initial /sm/ in the word *smile*.

2. Elicit the word *smile* from each child as the children draw smiles on the faces.

3. Send this art page home in each child's speech folder.

Optional Snack Activity

At the end of the session, set out a s'mores snack (e.g., S'mores cereal, s'mores Pop Tarts, s'mores granola bars). Have each child request a snack using a production based on his or her skill level. (As another option, make s'mores with the children using graham crackers, marshmallow creme, and chocolate bars.)

HOME PRACTICE

GOAL

To provide home suggestions for what the children can do in the context of their everyday lives

MATERIALS

1. Each child's set of colored target word illustrations

2. Each child's completed art pages

3. Each child's speech folder

4. Each child's *Family Letter*

PROCEDURE

1. Collect the children's colored target word illustrations and completed art pages, and send them home in their speech folders.

2. Write any special instructions specific to a child on the *Family Letter*, on the target word illustrations, or on the art pages.

smell

The snowman has a nice <u>smile</u>.

smoke

smash

Small or Large?

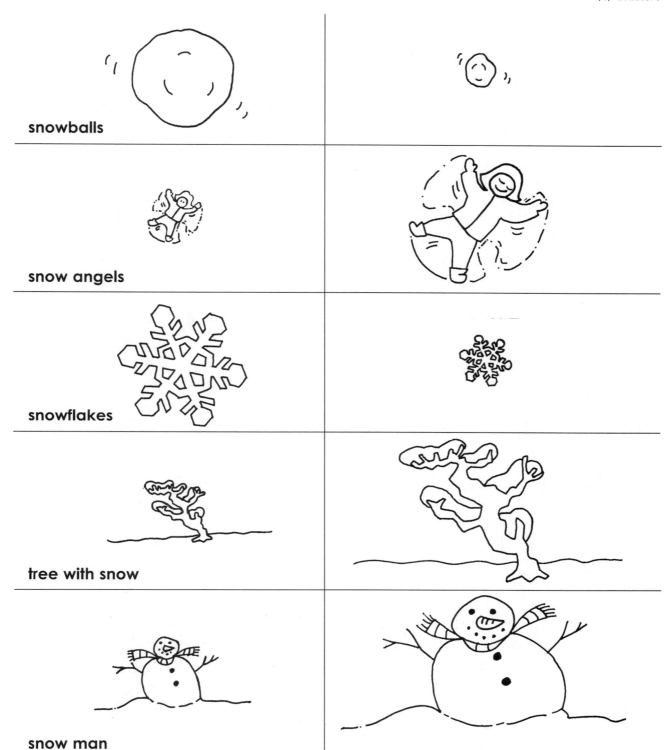

snowballs

snow angels

snowflakes

tree with snow

snow man

Circle the small picture and then tell its name. Is it small or large?

Talk about the smiles you made on the faces. Practice saying "smile."

Family Letter

Date: _____

Dear Family,

In this lesson, the emphasis is on producing the *sm* blend at the beginning of words. The *sm* blend is produced with the continuous airflow of the *s* sound in combination with the nasal quality of the *m* sound. When producing the *sm* blend, the children learn to "smile" and make the "hissing" snake sound. This "smile" position brings the upper and lower teeth together and helps eliminate sticking the tongue tip between the teeth (referred to as "the snake peeking out from between the teeth").

The book for this lesson is *The Snowy Day*, by Ezra Jack Keats. This book provides many opportunities for listening to words beginning with *sm* as well as other *s* blends. In this story, a little boy named Peter has lots of fun playing in the snow. He even tries to save a snowball by putting it in his pocket.

Listening List

Read this list to your child. Emphasize the *sm* blend at the beginning of each word.

small	smooth	smear	smock
smack	smart	smog	smother
smudge	smolder		

Target Words

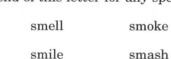

Using the pages in the speech folder, practice saying these words with your child. Follow the instructions provided at the end of this letter for any special considerations.

smell	smoke
smile	smash

Suggested Home Activities

1. Read the story *The Snowy Day* to your child. Slightly emphasize the *sm* blend at the beginning of the words *smacking* and *smiling*.

2. Play with a pretend camera. Have your child say *smile* while he or she takes pictures of people around the house.

3. Have your child smell different spices and other items with aromas. Help your child say the word *smell* each time he or she smells an item.

4. Look in your house for things that are big and small. Emphasize the *sm* blend in the word *small* when asking your child, *"Is this (ball) big or small?"* Help your child say the word *small* when responding to your question.

5. Smash pop cans for recycling. Model the *sm* blend while you talk about what you are doing (e.g., *"We are smashing pop cans"*).

6. Light a candle. Have your child blow it out and then help him or her say the word *smoke*.

7. Talk about the *Small or Large?* art page your child brings home. Help your child say the *sm* blend at the beginning of the word *small*.

8. Admire the *Smiley Faces* art page. Have your child point to each child and say *smile*.

Songs

The following songs are being practiced in class. Your can help your child use the *sm* blend by having him or her listen as you slightly emphasize the *sm* blend at the beginning of the underlined words.

"S'Mores"
(Sing to the tune of "Here We Go Round the Mulberry Bush.")

This is the way we make our <u>s'mores</u>.
We make our <u>s'mores</u>, we make our <u>s'mores</u>.
This is the way we make our <u>s'mores</u>,
when we are at school.

(Repeat with "This is the way we eat our <u>s'mores</u>...")

"It's a <u>Small</u> World"
(Show a globe or a small map of the world while singing the song.)

It's a <u>small</u> world after all.
It's a <u>small</u> world after all.
It's a <u>small</u> world after all.
It's a <u>small</u>, <u>small</u> world.

Special Considerations

Sincerely,

_____

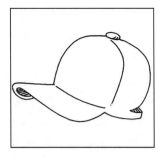

CAPS FOR SALE

PATTERN

/s/ clusters

TARGET CLUSTER

Word-final /ps/

TARGET WORDS

naps, caps, chips, hops

OPENING CENTER

GOAL

To introduce word-final /ps/

MATERIALS

1. One set of alphabet letters (Appendix C)

2. Book titled *Caps for Sale* (1968), by Esphyr Slobodkina

3. One straw per child and one per clinician

4. Mirror

Optional Materials

Bucket of objects such as several caps, toy children and animals to take naps

PROCEDURE

1. Introduce the letters *p* and *s* in the set of alphabet letters and demonstrate correct production of /p/ and /s/. Show the children how you blend /p/ and /s/ together. Sing the "Alphabet Song" (to the tune of "Twinkle, Twinkle, Little Star") and point to the letters *p* and *s* in the set of alphabet letters.

2. Show the children the letter *p* and help them produce /p/. Show the children the letter *s* and help them produce /s/. Then show the children the letters *p* and *s* together and help them produce the /ps/ cluster.

3. Introduce *Caps for Sale*. Point to the letter *p* and letter *s* in the title word *caps*. Have the children take turns finger-tracing the letters *p* and *s* as you say the word *caps*, slightly emphasizing the /ps/ cluster.

4. Read *Caps for Sale*. Slightly emphasize the /ps/ cluster when it occurs in the word *caps*. Model the role of the peddler (e.g., holler "Caps for sale!") and have the children imitate you as you read the story. Shake your index finger for the peddler telling the monkeys to give him back his caps. Shake your index finger to imitate the monkeys. Substitute "ps, ps, ps" for "tsz, tsz, tsz." Continue to imitate the motions of the peddler and the monkeys throughout the story.

5. Say the fingerplay "Farmer" and sing the song "The Ants Go Marching."

"Farmer"
First the farmer sows his seeds. *(Pretend to plant seeds.)*
Then he stands and takes his ease. *(Stand up.)*
He stamps his foot. *(Stamp your foot.)*
He claps his hands *(Clap your hands.)*
and turns around to view his lands. *(Turn around.)*

"The Ants Go Marching"
(Hold one finger up for one, two fingers up for two, etc.)

The ants go marching 1 by 1.
Hoorah, hoorah!
The ants go marching 1 by 1.
Hoorah, hoorah!
The ants go marching 1 by 1,
and the little one stops to suck his thumb.
And they all keep marching down…
to the ground…to get out…of the rain.
Boom, boom, boom, boom. Boom, boom, boom, boom.

(Repeat with "2 by 2…and the little one stops to tie his shoe…"
"3 by 3…and the little one stops to climb a tree…"
"4 by 4…and the little one stops to shut the door…"
"5 by 5…and the little one stops to sing and jive…"
"6 by 6…and the little one stops to pick up sticks…"
"7 by 7…and the little one stops to look to heaven…"
"8 by 8…and the little one stops to open the gate…"
"9 by 9…and the little one stops to scratch his spine…"
"10 by 10…and the little one stops to pet a hen.")*

LISTENING CENTER

GOAL

To provide clear auditory stimuli for word-final /ps/

MATERIALS

1. One amplifier and one connector with headset per child

2. Listening list: *lips, hopes, whoops, cups, dips, maps, keeps, tops, claps, wraps*

3. Illustrations of the four target words (pages 210–211; duplicate, cut out, and staple together)

4. Play dough

> **Optional Materials**
>
> *Cookie cutters shaped like the letters* p *and* s

PROCEDURE

1. Instruct the children to wear their headsets and to listen. Speak into the amplifier and read the listening list to the children.

2. Introduce the four target words—*naps, caps, chips, hops*—to the children using the illustrations.

3. Instruct the children to continue wearing their headsets as you present a model of each target word. Have the children take turns repeating each word after it has been presented to each of them.

4. Help the children make chips or cups from the play dough. Elicit the word *chips* or *cups* from each child.

> **Optional Activity**
>
> *Roll the play dough and help children cut out the letters* p *and* s *for* ps. *Elicit* /ps/ *from each child, as appropriate.*

PRACTICE CENTER

GOAL

To facilitate production of word-final /ps/

MATERIALS

1. One printed name card per child (see page 14)

2. Illustrations of the four target words (pages 210–211; duplicate, cut out, and staple together one set per child)

3. Colored markers

> **Optional Materials**
>
> *Stickers ending in* /ps/ *(e.g., caps or lips stickers) or stamps*

4. Each child's *Remediation Data Form* (Appendix B)

5. *Family Letter* (pages 214–215; duplicate one per child)

6. One speech folder per child

Optional Activity

Have the children choose several stickers or stamps to put on their folders. Then talk or ask questions about the stickers or stamps to model and elicit word-final /ps/ productions (e.g., "How many lips did you choose?" to elicit "I have two lips").

PROCEDURE

1. Have the children find their own name card. Once identified, instruct the children to finger-trace and say the letters in their names.

2. Instruct the children to color the four target word illustrations—*naps, caps, chips, hops*—using the colored markers.

3. Have the children take turns naming the target word illustrations. The goal is to elicit word-final /ps/.

4. Document the children's productions on their *Remediation Data Forms*.

5. Write notes related to each child's goal on his or her *Family Letter*.

ART CENTER

GOAL

To provide additional word-final /ps/ production practice and to create visual aids for home activities

MATERIAL

1. *Matching Caps* (page 212; duplicate one per child)

2. Colored pencils

3. *Hops, Hops, Hops!* (page 213; duplicate one per child)

4. One crayon per child

PROCEDURE

Matching Caps

1. Point to the cap at the top of the left column. Have the children put their fingers on the cap at the top. Then point to the matching cap. Have the children point to it also. Then show the children how to use the colored pencil to draw a line connecting the matching caps. Elicit the word *caps* from each child as they connect the matching caps. Do the same for the remaining caps.

2. Allow the children to color all the caps. Slightly emphasize /ps/ in the word *caps* as you talk about the caps while the children color.

3. Send this art page home in each child's speech folder.

Hops, Hops, Hops!

1. Identify the animals by name for the children. For each animal, ask the children if the animal hops. Model word-final /ps/ in the word *hops*. If the animal hops, have the children color the animal using their crayon.

2. Elicit the word *hops* from each child several times as the children color.

3. Send this art page home in each child's speech folder.

HOME PRACTICE

GOAL

To provide home suggestions for what the children can do in the context of their everyday lives

MATERIALS

1. Each child's set of colored target word illustrations

2. Each child's completed art pages

3. Each child's speech folder

4. Each child's *Family Letter*

PROCEDURE

1. Collect the children's colored target word illustrations and completed art pages, and send them home in their speech folders.

2. Write any special instructions specific to a child on the *Family Letter,* on the target word illustrations, or on the art pages.

> **Optional Snack Activity**
>
> *At the end of each session, set out some potato chips. Have each child request a snack using a production based on his or her skill level.*

naps

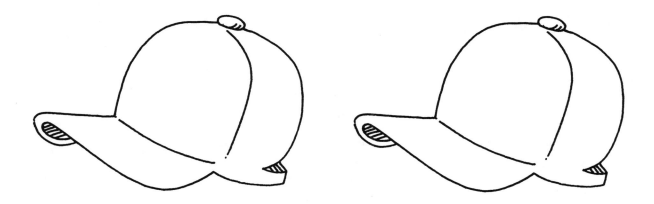

caps

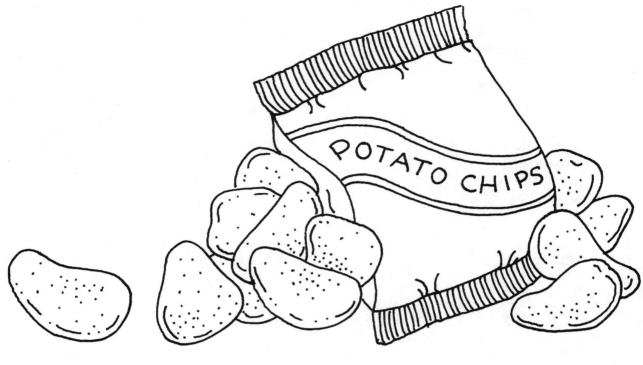

chips

hops

Color and talk about the matching caps.

birds

kangaroo

rabbit

mouse

squirrel

grasshopper

frog

Color each animal that hops.

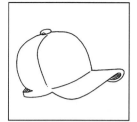

Date: _____

Dear Family,

In this lesson, the emphasis is on the *ps* blend at the end of words. This blend is a combination of the explosive *p* sound and the continuous airflow of the *s* sound. Several other aspects of your child's language may improve once he or she has learned how to use the *ps* blend. For example, plurals like *caps* and *maps*, possessives like the *pup's* collar and the *cup's* handle, and verbs like it *hops* and she *mops* all contain the *ps* blend at the end.

The book for this lesson is *Caps for Sale,* by Esphyr Slobodkina. The book is funny and it has lots of repetition. Children enjoy the familiar phrases "Caps! Caps for sale! Fifty cents a cap!" and "You monkeys, you. You give me back my caps." We change "Tsz, Tsz, Tsz!" to "Ps, Ps, Ps!" The children practice these phrases as they retell and act out the story.

Listening List

Read this list to your child. Slightly emphasize the *ps* blend at the end of each word.

lips	hopes	whoops	cups
dips	maps	keeps	tops
claps	wraps		

Target Words

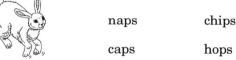

Using the pages in the speech folder, practice saying these words with your child. Follow the instructions provided at the end of this letter for any special considerations.

naps	chips
caps	hops

Suggested Home Activities

1. Read the story *Caps for Sale.* Slightly emphasize the final *ps* blend in the word *caps* when it occurs in the story.

2. Count potato chips with your child. Help your child say the *ps* blend in the word *chips* (e.g., *two chips, three chips*).

3. Count the cups in the cupboard. Help your child say *cups* when counting.

4. Look through animal books to find pictures of animals that hop. Have your child say "The (bunny) hops" as he or she finds animals that hop.

5. Talk about the *Matching Caps* art page. Have your child point to the caps that match and say *caps*.

6. Admire the *Hops, Hops, Hops!* art page your child brings home. Help your child say the word *hops* while pointing to each animal.

Fingerplays and Songs

The following fingerplay and song are being practiced in class. You can help your child use the *ps* blend by having him or her listen as you slightly emphasize the *ps* blend at the end of the underlined words.

"Farmer"

First the farmer sows his seeds. *(Pretend to plant seeds.)*
Then he stands and takes his ease. *(Stand up.)*
He <u>stamps</u> his foot. *(Stamp your foot.)*
He <u>claps</u> his hands *(Clap your hands.)*
and turns around to view his lands. *(Turn around.)*

"The Ants Go Marching"
(Hold one finger up for one, two fingers up for two, etc.)

The ants go marching 1 by 1.
Hoorah, hoorah!
The ants go marching 1 by 1.
Hoorah, hoorah!
The ants go marching 1 by 1,
and the little one <u>stops</u> to suck his thumb.
And they all keep marching down…
to the ground…to get out…of the rain.
Boom, boom, boom, boom. Boom, boom, boom, boom.

(Repeat with "2 by 2…and the little one <u>stops</u> to tie his shoe…"
　　　　　"3 by 3…and the little one <u>stops</u> to climb a tree…"
　　　　　"4 by 4…and the little one <u>stops</u> to shut the door…"
　　　　　"5 by 5…and the little one <u>stops</u> to sing and jive…"
　　　　　"6 by 6…and the little one <u>stops</u> to pick up sticks…"
　　　　　"7 by 7…and the little one <u>stops</u> to look to heaven…"
　　　　　"8 by 8…and the little one <u>stops</u> to open the gate…"
　　　　　"9 by 9…and the little one <u>stops</u> to scratch his spine…"
　　　　　"10 by 10…and the little one <u>stops</u> to pet a hen.")

Special Considerations

Sincerely,

_____

HOW DO YOU SAY IT TODAY, JESSE BEAR?

PATTERN

/s/ clusters

TARGET CLUSTER

Word-final /ts/

TARGET WORDS

hearts, boots, dots, hats

OPENING CENTER

GOAL

To introduce word-final /ts/

MATERIALS

<table>
<tr><td>Optional Materials</td></tr>
<tr><td>*Bucket of objects such as goats, bats, nuts, boats, cats, coats, skates, boots, hats, dots*</td></tr>
</table>

1. One set of alphabet letters

2. Book titled *How Do You Say It Today, Jesse Bear?* (1994), by Nancy White Carlstrom

3. One straw per child and one per clinician

4. Mirror

PROCEDURE

1. Introduce the letters *t* and *s* in the set of alphabet letters and demonstrate correct production of /t/ and /s/. Show the children how you blend /t/ and /s/ together. Sing the "Alphabet Song" (to the tune of "Twinkle, Twinkle, Little Star") and point to the letters *t* and *s* in the set of alphabet letters.

2. Show the children the letter *t* and help them produce /t/. Show the children the letter *s* and help them produce /s/. Then show the children the letters *t* and *s* together and help them produce the /ts/ cluster.

3. Read *How Do You Say It Today*, *Jesse Bear?* Emphasize word-final /ts/ in the words *hearts* and *kites*. Find pictures within the story containing word-final /ts/ (e.g., pots, hats, rabbits, boats, flutes, shirts, beets, lights, boots, skates). Model and elicit word-final /ts/ productions when talking about these objects.

4. Sing the songs "Kites Are Flying in the Sky" and "Hokey Pokey."

"Kites Are Flying in the Sky"
(Sing to the tune of "Airplanes Flying in the Sky.")

Kites are flying in the sky. Zoom! Zoom!
Kites are flying in the sky. Zoom! Zoom!
Round and round the kites will go.
Flying high. Flying low. Zoom!
(Pretend to be a kite and fly high and low.)

"Hokey Pokey"
(Form a circle with the children. Use signs, gestures, or actual objects for the names of the items.)

We put our hats in.
(Hold hats inside the circle.)
We put our hats out.
(Hold hats outside the circle.)
We put our hats in and we shake them all about.
(Hold hats inside the circle and shake them.)
We do the Hokey Pokey and we turn ourselves around.
(Wave your arms up and down while you turn in a circle.)
That's what it's all about.
(Clap your hands six times along with each syllable.)

(Repeat the song several times substituting "coats," "skates," "mats," etc. for hats.)

Helpful Hints

For children having difficulty producing /s/ because they lateralize the production, it is often helpful and motivating for them to hear the stream of air going through the straw when /s/ is produced. Demonstrate the "hissing" sound made when the straw is placed in front of the teeth and air is produced. Then have children imitate the same with their straws. For children who are interdentalizing /s/ production, direct them to place their tongue as though they will produce /t/ and then slide their tongues back to an /s/ position. Use the mirror to facilitate correct teeth and lip placement.

Optional Activity

Have the children close their eyes and reach into the bucket for an object. Model the name of the object, articulating word-final /ts/. Have the children produce the word or word approximation after you model.

LISTENING CENTER

GOAL

To provide clear auditory stimuli for word-final /ts/

MATERIALS

1. One amplifier and one connector with headset per child

2. Listening list: *bats, boats, coats, cats, kites, nuts, mats, pots, beets, lights*

3. Illustrations of the four target words (pages 221–222; duplicate, cut out, and staple together)

4. Play dough

5. One toothpick per child

PROCEDURE

1. Instruct the children to wear their headsets and to listen. Speak into the amplifier and read the listening list to the children.

2. Introduce the four target words—*hearts, boots, dots, hats*—to the children using the illustrations.

3. Instruct the children to continue wearing their headsets as you present a model of each target word. Have the children take turns repeating each word after it has been presented to each them.

4. Help the children roll the play dough into a ball. Model the word *dots* as the children use their toothpicks to poke dots into the play dough ball.

PRACTICE CENTER

GOAL

To facilitate production of word-final /ts/

MATERIALS

1. One printed name card per child (see page 14)

2. Illustrations of the four target words (pages 221–222; duplicate, cut out, and staple together one set per child)

3. Colored markers

4. Each child's *Remediation Data Form* (Appendix B)

5. *Family Letter* (pages 225–226; duplicate one per child)

6. One speech folder per child

PROCEDURE

1. Have the children find their own name card. Once identified, instruct the children to finger-trace and say the letters in their names.

2. Instruct the children to color the four target word illustrations—*hearts, boots, dots, hats*—using the colored markers.

3. Have the children take turns naming the target word illustrations. The goal is to elicit word-final /ts/.

4. Document the children's productions on their *Remediation Data Form*.

5. Write notes related to each child's goal on his or her *Family Letter*.

ART CENTER

GOAL

To provide additional word-final /ts/ production practice and to create visual aids for home activities

MATERIALS

1. *Dots on Hearts* (page 223; duplicate one per child)

2. Crayons

3. *More Than One* (page 224; duplicate one per child)

4. One colored pencil per child

PROCEDURE

Dots on Hearts

1. Talk to the children about the different-sized hearts on the page. Using crayons, demonstrate how to put colorful dots on the different-shaped hearts. Emphasize /ts/ in the words *hearts* and *dots*.

2. Have the children decorate their hearts with colorful dots. Elicit the words *hearts* and *dots* from each child as the children color. Tell the children to make a heart note to take home. Using their colored pencil, help the children write I ❤ U (I love you) on the back of the art page.

More Than One

1. Discuss the concept of more than one to the children. Explain that when there is more than one of the same object, an *s* is often added to the object's name.

2. Tell the children to point to the top row on their sheets and to compare the two boxes in the top row.

3. Have the children use the colored pencil to circle the box with more than one kite. Elicit the word *kites* from the children as they circle the three kites.

4. Continue this process for each row on the page.

> **Optional Snack Activity**
>
> *At the end of the session, set out some candy Dots. Have each child request a snack using a production based on his or her skill level.*

HOME PRACTICE

GOAL

To provide home suggestions for what the children can do in the context of their everyday lives

MATERIALS

1. Each child's set of colored target word illustrations

2. Each child's completed art pages

3. Each child's speech folder

4. Each child's *Family Letter*

PROCEDURE

1. Collect the children's colored target word illustrations and completed art pages, and send them home in their speech folders.

2. Write any special instructions specific to a child on the *Family Letter*, on the target word illustrations, or on the art pages.

hearts

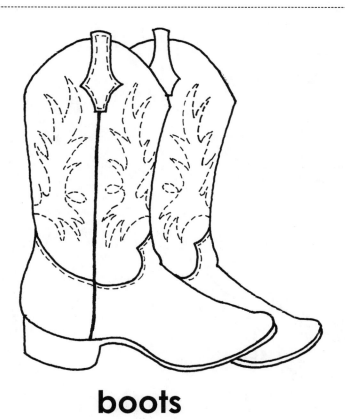

boots

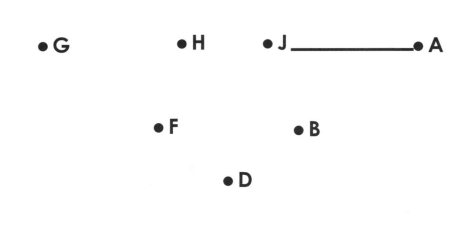

Connect the *dots*.

hats

Make the hearts colorful by covering them with dots. Say "dots" when you color.

Talk about the pictures
that show more than one.

Family Letter

Date: _____

Dear Family,

In this lesson, the emphasis is on producing the *ts* blend at the end of words. This blend is a combination of the explosive *t* sound and the continuous airflow of the *s* sound. Several other aspects of your child's language may improve once he or she has learned how to use the *ts* blend. For example, plurals like *cats* and *mats*, possessives like the *cat's* collar and Matt's *shoe* and verbs like he *sits* and she *hits* all contain the *ts* blend at the end of words.

The book for this lesson is *How Do You Say It Today, Jesse Bear?* by Nancy White Carlstrom. This story follows Jesse Bear as he finds objects, such as pots, hats, rabbits, and boats. There are many opportunities for your child to hear the *ts* sound at the end of words when you talk about the pictures on the pages.

Listening List

Read this list to your child. Slightly emphasize the *ts* blend at the end of each word.

bats	boats	coats	cats
kites	nuts	mats	pots
beets	lights		

Target Words

Using the pages in the speech folder, practice saying these words with your child. Follow the instructions provided at the end of this letter for any special considerations.

hearts	dots
boots	hats

Suggested Home Activities

1. Read the story *How Do You Say It Today, Jesse Bear?* to your child. Slightly emphasize the *ts* blend at the end of the words *hearts* and *kites*. There are many pictures to find in the story that contain the *ts* blend: *pots, hats, rabbits, boats, flutes, beets, lights, boots* and *skates*. Find these pictures with your child and name them.

2. Help your child make hearts from play dough or cookie dough. Count the number of hearts you make. If desired, decorate the cookies with dots (play dough or candy). Slightly emphasize the words *dots* and *hearts* as you play.

3. Play dress-up. Emphasize the *ts* blend while you talk about the different *hats, coats, shirts,* and *boots* you try on.

4. Admire the *Dots on Hearts* art page your child brings home. Help your child say the words *dots* and *hearts* as the two of you talk about the page.

5. Review the *More Than One* art page. Have your child name the pictures that show more than one (e.g., *kites, hearts, cats,* etc.).

Songs

These songs are being practiced in class. You can help your child use the *ts* blend by having him or her listen as you slightly emphasize the *ts* blend at the beginning of the underlined words.

"Kites Are Flying in the Sky"

(Sing to the tune of "Airplanes Flying in the Sky.")

<u>Kites</u> are flying in the sky. Zoom! Zoom!
<u>Kites</u> are flying in the sky. Zoom! Zoom!
Round and round the <u>kites</u> will go.
Flying high. Flying low. Zoom!
(Pretend to be a kite and fly high and low.)

"Hokey Pokey"

(Stand facing your child. Use gestures, signs, or actual objects for the names of the items.)

We put our <u>hats</u> in.
(Hold hats in front of you.)
We put our <u>hats</u> out.
(Hold hats behind you.)
We put our <u>hats</u> in and we shake them all about.
(Hold hats in front of you and shake them.)
We do the Hokey Pokey and we turn ourselves around.
(Wave your arms up and down while you turn in a circle.)
<u>That's</u> what <u>it's</u> all about.
(Clap your hands six times along with each syllable.)

(Repeat the song several times substituting "coats," "skates," "mats," etc. for hats.)

Special Considerations

Sincerely,

_____

PRIMARY TARGET
PATTERNS: LIQUIDS

QUICK AS A CRICKET

PATTERN

Liquids

TARGET PHONEME

Word-initial /l/

TARGET WORDS

loud, "la-la-la," lark, light

OPENING CENTER

GOAL

To introduce word-initial /l/

MATERIALS

1. One set of alphabet letters (Appendix C)

2. Mirror

3. Book titled *Quick as a Cricket* (1982), by Audrey Wood

PROCEDURE

1. Introduce the letter *l* in the set of alphabet letters and demonstrate correct production of /l/. Sing the "Alphabet Song" (to the tune of "Twinkle, Twinkle, Little Star") and point to the letter *l* in the set of alphabet letters.

2. Have the children produce /l/ while looking in the mirror.

3. Read *Quick as a Cricket*. Model word-initial /l/ in the words *lion, loud,* and *lamb.*

Optional Materials

Bucket of objects such as a ladder, a lizard, a lemon, a lion, a log, a light, lettuce

---

Helpful Hints

Ask the children to drop their jaws open. Some children may need help to stabilize the jaw in this open position. First have the children sustain /l/, then "la-la-la" to practice the tongue movement for /l/. Another helpful activity is "tongue clicking." Instruct the children to suck up the tongue tip to the alveolar ridge area and then quickly release to hear a "click" sound. This sucking up of the tongue helps to coordinate independent jaw and tongue movement to facilitate production of /l/.

4. Sing the songs "London Bridge" and "Mary Had a Little Lamb."

"London Bridge"

London Bridge is falling down,
falling down, falling down.
London Bridge is falling down,
my fair lady (and/or laddie).

"Mary Had a Little Lamb"

Mary had a little lamb,
little lamb, little lamb.
Mary had a little lamb,
whose fleece was white as snow.

LISTENING CENTER

GOAL

To provide clear auditory stimuli for word-initial /l/

MATERIALS

1. One amplifier and one connector with headset per child

2. Listening list: *low, lip, lap, lamp, line, late, leaf, laugh, lake, leg*

3. Illustrations of the four target words (pages 234–235; duplicate, cut out, and staple together)

4. Play dough

5. One popsicle stick per child

PROCEDURE

1. Instruct the children to wear their headsets and to listen. Speak into the amplifier and read the listening list to the children.

2. Introduce the four target words—*loud, "la-la-la," lark, light*—to the children using the illustrations.

3. Instruct the children to continue wearing their headsets as you present a model of each target word. Have the children take turns repeating each word after it has been presented to each of them.

4. Help the children make lollipops. Have the children roll the play dough into a ball and then push the end of the popsicle stick into it. The children can pretend to lick the lollipop. Elicit the word *lick* or *lollipop* from each child.

PRACTICE CENTER

GOAL

To facilitate production of word-initial /l/

MATERIALS

1. One printed name card per child (see page 14)

2. Illustrations of the four target words (pages 234–235; duplicate, cut out, and staple together one set per child)

3. Colored markers

4. Each child's *Remediation Data Form* (Appendix B)

5. *Family Letter* (pages 238–239; duplicate one per child)

6. One speech folder per child

PROCEDURE

1. Have the children find their own name card. Once identified, instruct the children to finger-trace and say the letters in their names.

2. Instruct the children to color the four target word illustrations—*loud, "la-la-la," lark, light*—using the colored markers.

3. Have the children take turns naming the target word illustrations. The goal is to elicit word-initial /l/.

4. Document the children's productions on their *Remediation Data Forms*.

5. Write notes related to each child's goal on his or her *Family Letter*.

Optional Activity

Have the children choose a sticker to put on their folders. Then talk or ask questions about the sticker to elicit word-initial /l/ productions (e.g., "Which animal is the king of the forest?" to elicit "The lion").

ART CENTER

GOAL

To provide additional word-initial /l/ production practice and to create visual aids for home activities

MATERIALS

1. *Loud as a Lion* (page 236; duplicate one per child)

2. Yellow watercolor paint

3. One paintbrush per child

4. *La-La Lines* (page 237; duplicate one per child)

5. Yellow and blue soft crayons (Craypas)

PROCEDURE

Loud as a Lion

1. Have the children use the watercolors to paint the lion's mane yellow. Instruct the children to say the words *lion* and *long* as they paint the long mane. Make sure each child lifts his or her tongue tip to the alveolar ridge upon initiating /l/. Talk about how loud the lion can be.

2. Allow the art page to dry, and then send it home in the child's speech folder the following session.

La-La Lines

1. Help the children trace each line with a yellow or blue soft crayon. As the children trace the four lines, model the following:

   Straight line: Instruct the children to sustain one continuous "la" as they color the line.

   Curvy line: Instruct the children to sing "la" up and down the curvy line. You may want to model various pitch levels as the children color up and down the curvy line.

   Zigzag line: Instruct the children to say "la" each time they zig or zag along the line.

   Dotted line: Instruct the children to use a sharp, staccato "la" for each of the short dotted lines.

2. Send this art page home in each child's speech folder.

HOME PRACTICE

GOAL

To provide home suggestions for what the children can do in the context of their everyday lives

MATERIALS

1. Each child's set of colored target word illustrations

2. Each child's completed art pages

3. Each child's speech folder

4. Each child's *Family Letter*

PROCEDURE

1. Collect the children's colored target word illustrations and completed art pages, and send them home in their speech folders.

2. Write any special instructions specific to a child on the *Family Letter*, on the target word illustrations, or on the art pages.

Optional Snack Activity

At the end of the session, set out lemon lollipops. Have each child request a snack using a production based on his or her skill level. Some children may say /lɑ/ or /lɑ-li/. More advanced children may say "Lollipop, please" or "I would like a lollipop."

Loud as a lion.

La-la-la

Mary's lamb says, "La-la-la."

Happy as a lark.

light

**Paint the lion's long mane yellow.
Talk about the lion's long mane and
how loud a lion can be.**

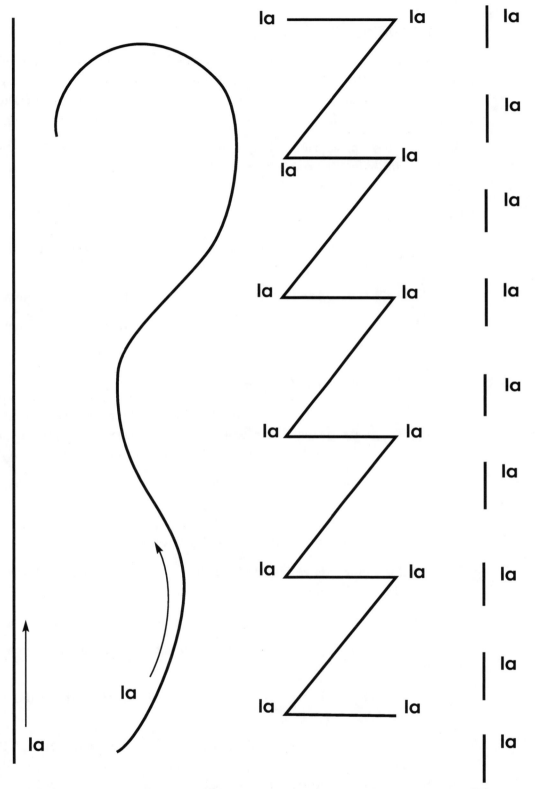

Say "la" while you color the lines.

Date: _____

Dear Family,

The focus for this lesson is on the *l* sound. This sound is made when the tip of the tongue touches the bumpy ridge behind the upper front teeth. There is an uninterrupted flow of air for correct production. It sometimes helps to ask children to drop their jaw then lift their tongue tip to the bumpy spot behind their top teeth.

For this lesson, the charming story *Quick as a Cricket*, by Audrey Wood, will be read. The full-page illustrations show a young child informing his readers and himself of all the wonderful things he can do and feel.

Listening List

Read this list to your child. Slightly emphasize the *l* sound at the beginning of each word.

low	lip	lap	lamp
line	late	leaf	laugh
lake	leg		

Target Words

Using the pages in the speech folder, practice saying these words with your child. Follow the instructions provided at the end of this letter for any special considerations.

loud	lark
"la-la-la"	light

Suggested Home Activities

1. Read the story *Quick as a Cricket* to your child. Slightly emphasize the *l* sound at the beginning of the word *loud*.

2. Lick lollipops. Help your child say the words *lick* and *lollipop*.

3. Play leapfrog. Practice saying the word *leap* each time you or your child leaps.

4. Let your child help you lick stamps and envelopes. Have your child say the word *lick*.

5. Have your child tell someone what foods he or she likes: "I *like*..." If your child does not correctly produce the *l* at the beginning of words, have him or her listen to your correct productions.

6. Using the *La-La Lines* art page, help your child correctly lift his or her tongue tip to say *"la-la-la"* while finger-tracing the lines.

7. Admire the *Loud as a Lion* art page. Have your child listen to you clearly articulate the words *loud, long,* and *lion.* Talk about how loud a lion can be.

Songs

The following songs are being practiced in class. You can help your child use the *l* sound by having him or her listen as you slightly emphasize the *l* sound at the beginning of the underlined words.

"London Bridge"

<u>London</u> Bridge is falling down,
falling down, falling down.
<u>London</u> Bridge is falling down,
my fair <u>lady</u> (and/or <u>laddie</u>).

"Mary Had a Little Lamb"

Mary had a <u>little</u> <u>lamb</u>,
<u>little</u> <u>lamb</u>, <u>little</u> <u>lamb</u>.
Mary had a <u>little</u> <u>lamb</u>,
whose fleece was white as snow.

Special Considerations

Sincerely,

_____

IT LOOKED LIKE SPILT MILK

PATTERN

Liquids

TARGET PHONEME

Word-initial /l/

TARGET WORDS

lick, look, like, lake

OPENING CENTER

GOAL

To introduce word-initial /l/

Optional Materials

Bucket of objects such as a lion, a lamb, lollipops for "lick," a leaf, a leash, a lock

MATERIALS

1. One set of alphabet letters (Appendix C)
2. Book titled *It Looked Like Spilt Milk* (1947), by Charles G. Shaw

PROCEDURE

1. Introduce the letter *l* in the set of alphabet letters and demonstrate correct production of /l/. Sing the "Alphabet Song" (to the tune of "Twinkle, Twinkle, Little Star") and point to the letter *l* in the set of alphabet letters.

2. Read *It Looked Like Spilt Milk*. Model word-initial /l/ in the words *looked* and *like*.

3. Sing the songs "Did You Ever See a Lassie?" and "Love Somebody, Yes I Do."

"Did You Ever See a Lassie?"

(Sway back and forth as you sing this song.)

Did you ever see a lassie, a lassie, a lassie?

Did you ever see a lassie, go this way and that?

Go this way and that way.

And this way and that way.

Did you ever see a lassie, go this way and that?

(Repeat with "Did you ever see a laddie, a laddie, a laddie…")

"Love Somebody, Yes I Do"

(Sing to the tune of "I'm a Nut!")

Love somebody, yes I do.

Love somebody, yes I do.

Love somebody, yes I do.

Love somebody, but I won't tell who.

(Repeat with "Love my Daddy, yes I do…," "Love my Mommy, yes I do…,"
"Love my Gramma, yes I do…," "Love my Grandpa, yes I do.")

LISTENING CENTER

GOAL

To provide clear auditory stimuli for word-initial /l/

MATERIALS

1. One amplifier and one connector with headset per child

2. Listening list: *leak, late, laugh, lift, long, lane, limb, lit, loud*

3. Illustrations of the four target words (pages 245–246; duplicate, cut out, and staple together)

4. Play dough

PROCEDURE

1. Instruct the children to wear their headsets and to listen. Speak into the amplifier and read the listening list to the children.

2. Introduce the four target words—*lick, look, like, lake*—to the children using the illustrations.

Helpful Hints

To facilitate production of /l/, ask the children to drop their jaw and then lift the tongue tip to the bumpy spot behind the upper teeth.

Optional Activity

Have the children close their eyes and reach into the bucket for an object. Model the name of the object, articulating word-initial /l/. Have the children produce the word or word approximation after your model.

Optional Materials

Toy boats

Optional Activity

Fill a big pan full of water. Have the children float their toy boats on a pretend lake.

3. Instruct the children to continue wearing their headsets as you present a model of each target word. Have the children take turns repeating each word after it has been presented to each of them.

4. Have the children use the play dough to form shapes. Model the sentence, "It looks like _____", or have them make ice-cream cones or lollipops and pretend to lick them.

PRACTICE CENTER

GOAL

To facilitate production of word-initial /l/

Optional Materials

Lollipop stickers

MATERIALS

1. One printed name card per child (see page 14)

2. Illustrations of the four target words (pages 245–246; duplicate, cut out, and staple together one set per child)

3. Colored markers

4. Each child's *Remediation Data Form* (Appendix B)

5. *Family Letter* (pages 250–251; duplicate one per child)

6. One speech folder per child

Optional Activity

Have the children choose a lollipop sticker to put on their folders. Then use a cloze procedure to elicit "Lollipop" by saying, "Let's pretend to lick your _____ stickers."

PROCEDURE

1. Have the children find their own name card. Once identified, instruct the children to finger-trace and say the letters in their names.

2. Have the children color the four target word illustrations—*lick, look, like, lake*—using colored markers.

3. Have the children take turns naming the target word illustrations. The goal is to elicit word-initial /l/.

4. Document the children's productions on their *Remediation Data Forms*.

5. Write notes related to each child's goal on his or her *Family Letter.*

ART CENTER

GOAL

To provide additional word-initial /l/ production practice and to create visual aids for home activities

MATERIALS

1. *Sometimes They Look Like…* (page 247; duplicate one per child on light blue colored paper)

2. One piece of white chalk per child

3. *Lollipop Lane Game Board* (page 248; duplicate one for classroom use)

4. Crayons

5. *Game Pieces* (see page 249; duplicate one for classroom use)

6. One lollipop per child

PROCEDURE

Sometimes They Look Like…

1. Instruct each child to use the white chalk to color the cloud shapes.

2. Ask each child what he or she thinks the clouds look like. Write the child's responses near each picture.

3. Model and elicit word-initial /l/ in the words *lion, leaf, lip, lamp, lollipop, lamb, lake,* and *light.*

4. Send this art page home in each child's speech folder.

Lollipop Lane Game Board

1. Tell the children to color the word-initial /l/ pictures on the game board and to color the game pieces.

2. Model the name of each picture as the children color.

3. After the game pieces are colored, cut them out. Stack them on the game board on the framed lollipops.

4. Have each child take a turn choosing a game piece and matching it to the appropriate picture on the game board.

5. Model the name of the game piece and elicit word-initial /l/ in the words *leaf, lollipop, light, log, lake, lion, lamp, lip,* and *lamb* as the children choose the pieces and match them.

243

6. When all the game pieces have been matched, give each child a lollipop. Declare everyone a winner!

Optional Snack Activity

At the end of the session, set out pieces of licorice and lollipops to lick. Have each child request a snack using a production based on his or her skill level.

HOME PRACTICE

GOAL

To provide home suggestions for what the children can do in the context of their everyday lives

MATERIALS

1. Each child's set of colored target word illustrations

2. Each child's completed art page

3. Each child's speech folder

4. Each child's *Family Letter*

PROCEDURE

1. Collect the children's colored target word illustrations and completed art page, and send them home in their speech folders.

2. Write any special instructions specific to a child on the *Family Letter*, on the target word illustrations, or on the art page.

lick

look

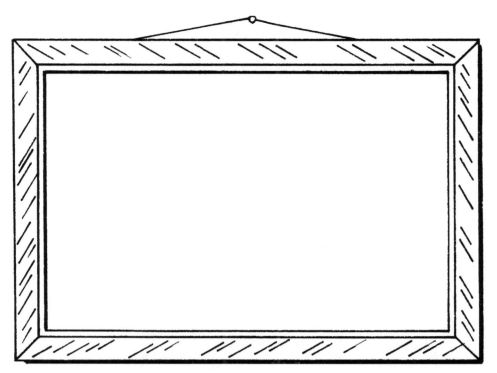

I like _____.

lake

Color the clouds with chalk.
What do the clouds look like?

Lollipop Lane Game Board

Game Pieces

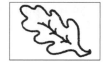  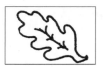 

Family Letter

Date: _____

Dear Family,

The focus for this lesson is on saying the *l* sound at the beginning of words. To help children make the *l* sound, we tell them to drop their jaw and then lift the tip of their tongue to the bumpy spot behind their upper teeth.

The book *It Looked Like Spilt Milk,* by Charles G. Shaw, was chosen to provide practice listening to and saying the *l*. This story offers many opportunities for children to use their imaginations and talk about the shapes of the clouds. The sentence, "Sometimes they look like a _____," is repeated throughout the story.

Listening List

Read this list to your child. Slightly emphasize the *l* sound at the beginning of each word.

leak	late	laugh	lift
long	lane	limb	lit
light	loud		

Target Words

Using the pages in the speech folder, practice saying these words with your child. Follow the instructions provided at the end of this letter for any special considerations.

lick	like
look	lake

Suggested Home Activities

1. Read the story *It Looked Like Spilt Milk* to your child. Slightly emphasize the *l* sound at the beginning of the words *looked* and *like*. Have your child imitate the words as you say them.

2. Lie on your back and look at the clouds. Help your child say the words *lie* and *look*. Talk about what the clouds look like.

3. Make a leaf collage. Help your child say *leaf* for each leaf pasted in the collage.

4. Look for all the items in your kitchen that begin with *l* (e.g., *lemon, light, lettuce*). Help your child say the *l* sound in the items found.

5. Review the *Sometimes They Look Like…* art page. Help your child say what each cloud looks like.

Songs

The following songs are being practiced in class. You can help your child use the *l* sound by having him or her listen as you slightly emphasize the *l* sound at the beginning of the underlined words.

"Did You Ever See a <u>Lassie</u>?"
(Sway back and forth as you sing this song.)

Did you ever see a <u>lassie</u>, a <u>lassie</u>, a <u>lassie</u>?
Did you ever see a <u>lassie</u>, go this way and that?
Go this way and that way.
And this way and that way.
Did you ever see a <u>lassie</u>, go this way and that?

(Repeat with "Did you ever see a laddie, a laddie, a laddie…")

"<u>Love</u> Somebody, Yes I Do"
(Sing to the tune of "I'm a Nut.")

<u>Love</u> somebody, yes I do.
<u>Love</u> somebody, yes I do.
<u>Love</u> somebody, yes I do.
<u>Love</u> somebody, but I won't tell who.

(Repeat with "<u>Love</u> my Daddy, yes I do…, <u>Love</u> my Mommy, yes I do…, <u>Love</u> my Gramma, yes I do…, and <u>Love</u> my Grandpa, yes I do….)

Special Considerations

Sincerely,

_____

RED IS BEST

PATTERN

Liquids

TARGET PHONEME

Word-initial /r/

TARGET WORDS

read, row, run, ride

OPENING CENTER

GOAL

To introduce word-initial /r/

Optional Materials
Bucket of objects such as a rose, a robot, a rocket, rice, a rope, a rock, a ribbon, a ring, a rug, a rabbit

MATERIALS

1. One set of alphabet letters (Appendix C)

2. Book titled *Red Is Best* (1992), by Kathy Stinson

PROCEDURE

1. Introduce the letter *r* in the set of alphabet letters and demonstrate correct production of /r/. Sing the "Alphabet Song" (to the tune of "Twinkle, Twinkle, Little Star") and point to the letter *r* in the set of alphabet letters.

2. Introduce *Red Is Best*. Point out the letter *r* in the title word *red*.

3. Read *Red Is Best*. Model word-initial /r/ in the words *red*, *Red Riding Hood*, *rainy*, etc.

4. Say the rhyme "Roses Are Red" and sing the song "Hokey Pokey."

"Roses Are Red"

Roses are red.

Violets are blue.

Sugar is sweet

and so are you!

"Hokey Pokey"

(Form a circle with everyone facing the center of the circle.)

You put your right foot in.

(Set right foot inside the circle.)

Your put your right foot out.

(Set right foot outside the circle.)

You put your right foot in,

(Set right foot inside the circle.)

and you shake it all about.

(Shake right foot inside circle.)

You do the hokey pokey and you turn yourself around.

(Shake your hands in the air as you take 8 small steps to turn around.)

That's what it's all about!

(Clap as you sing.)

(Repeat with "left foot…," "right arm…," "left arm…," etc.)

Optional Activity

Have the children close their eyes and reach into the bucket for an object. Model the name of the object. Label the toy for the children articulating the word-initial /r/. Have the children produce the word or word approximation after a model.

LISTENING CENTER

GOAL

To provide clear auditory stimuli for word-initial /r/

MATERIALS

1. One amplifier and one connector with headset per child

2. Listening list: *red, rock, rake, rug, rope, rice, ring, rabbit, ribbon, radio*

3. Illustrations of the four target words (pages 257–258; duplicate, cut out, and staple together)

4. Red play dough

Optional Materials

Cookie cutters shaped like the letter r

PROCEDURE

1. Instruct the children to wear their headsets and to listen. Speak into the amplifier and read the listening list to the children.

2. Introduce the four target words—*read, row, run, ride*—to the children using the illustrations.

3. Instruct the children to continue wearing their headsets as you present a model of each target word. Have the children take turns repeating each word after it has been presented to each of them.

4. Roll the red play dough. Make a rope from the play dough. Make a ring from the play dough. Make pretend rocks from the play dough. Model and elicit word-initial /r/ in the words *roll, red, rope, ring,* and *rock*.

PRACTICE CENTER

GOAL

To facilitate production of word-initial /r/

MATERIALS

1. One printed name card per child (see page 14)

2. Illustrations of the four target words (pages 257–258; duplicate, cut out, and staple together one set per child)

3. Colored markers

4. Each child's *Remediation Data Form* (Appendix B)

5. *Family Letter* (pages 261–262; duplicate one per child)

6. One speech folder per child

PROCEDURE

1. Have the children find their own name card. Once identified, instruct the children to finger-trace and say the letters in their names.

2. Instruct the children to color the four target word illustrations—*read, row, run, ride*—using the colored markers.

3. Have the children take turns naming the target word illustrations. The goal is to elicit word-initial /r/.

4. Document the children's productions on their *Remediation Data Forms*.

5. Write notes related to each child's goal on his or her *Family Letter*.

ART CENTER

GOAL

To provide additional word-initial /r/ production practice and to create visual aids for home activities

MATERIALS

1. *Rosie's Room* (page 259; duplicate one per child)

2. One red crayon per child

3. *Rock Garden* (page 260; duplicate one per child)

4. One red colored pencil per child

PROCEDURE

Rosie's Room

1. Describe the *Rosie's Room* art page to the children.

2. Instruct the children to find all the objects on the page that were red in the book and to color them red. Model and elicit word-initial /r/ in the word *red*.

3. Send this art page home in each child's speech folder.

Rock Garden

1. Help the children find the hidden objects in the rock garden. Remind the children that the hidden objects all begin with /r/.

2. Tell the children to circle or color the hidden word-initial /r/ objects using their red pencils.

3. Send this art page home in each child's speech folder.

HOME PRACTICE

GOAL

To provide home suggestions for what the children can do in the context of their everyday lives

Optional Snack Activity

At the end of the session, set out a snack beginning with /r/ (e.g., red apple, Red Hots, Big Red gum, Ritz crackers). Have each child request a snack using a production based on his or her skill level.

MATERIALS

1. Each child's set of colored target word illustrations

2. Each child's completed art pages

3. Each child's speech folder

4. Each child's *Family Letter*

PROCEDURE

1. Collect the children's colored target word illustrations and completed art pages, and send them home in their speech folders.

2. Write any special instructions specific to a child on the *Family Letter*, on the target word illustrations, or on the art pages.

read

row

run

ride

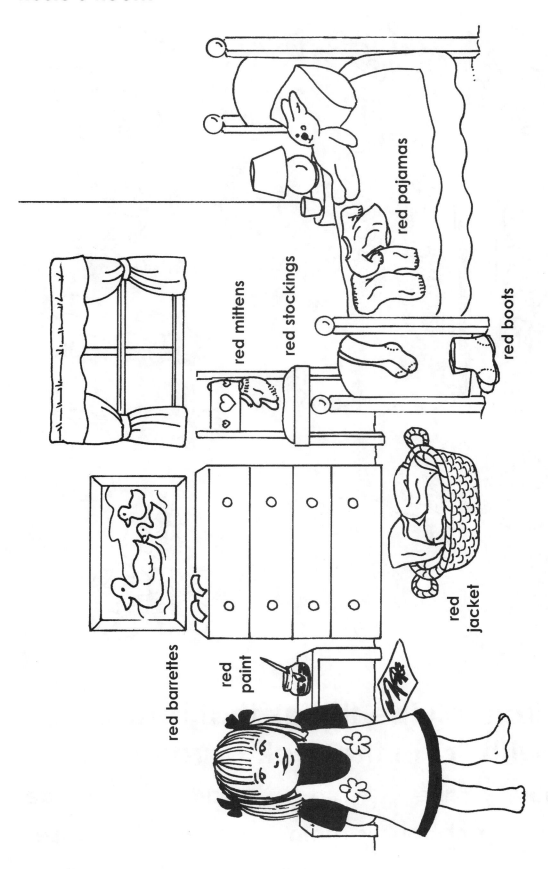

red pajamas

red mittens

red stockings

red boots

red jacket

red barrettes

red paint

Help Rosie find everything red in her room.

Rock Garden

Circle all the things that begin with "r" in the rock garden.

- rabbit
- rake
- rug
- radio
- rope
- ring
- ribbon
- robin
- rice
- rose

Family Letter

Date: _____

Dear Family,

In this lesson, the *r* sound at the beginning of words is introduced. The *r* sound is formed by raising the tip of the tongue toward the teeth ridge. The tip is turned slightly backward and the sides of the tongue touch the upper inside gums. Children often enjoy practicing the *r* sound by making a rooster call "r-r-r-r-r!"

At the early stages of saying this sound, an approximation of *r* is acceptable. Words beginning with *r* can be broke apart, so *red* becomes *r...ed*. This helps prevent the children from producing a *w* instead of *r*. Later the children learn to blend the sounds together. Also, to help children produce *r*, they are told to "smile" when making the sound. This helps prevent rounding of the lips, which is typically done when saying a *w* sound.

The story for this lesson is *Red Is Best,* by Kathy Stinson. This story is about a young child who tries to convince her mother that absolutely nothing is better than the color red.

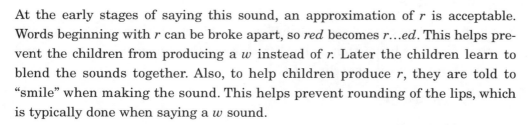

Listening List

Read this list to your child. Slightly emphasize the *r* sound at the beginning of each word.

rat	rock	rake	rug
rope	rice	ring	rabbit
ribbon	radio		

Target Words

Using the pages in the speech folder, practice saying these words with your child. Follow the instructions provided at the end of this letter for any special considerations.

read	run
row	ride

Suggested Home Activities

1. Read the story *Red is Best* to your child. Slightly emphasize the *r* sound at the beginning of the word *red*. As you read, ask your child to point to pictures of red items in the story.

2. Talk about the things you can read (newspaper, cereal boxes, street signs). Help your child say the word *read*.

3. Talk about red things around the house (red apples, red cherries, red tomatoes).

4. Admire the *Rosie's Room* art page. Help your child say the word *red f*or each red item colored.

5. Review the *Rock Garden* art page. Help your child name all the things that begin with *r* in the rock garden.

Rhymes and Songs

The following rhyme and song are being practiced in class. You can help your child use the *r* sound by having him or her listen as you slightly emphasize the *r* sound at the beginning of the underlined words.

"<u>Roses</u> Are <u>Red</u>"

<u>Roses</u> are <u>red</u>
violets are blue
sugar is sweet
and so are you!

"Hokey Pokey"

(Form a circle with everyone facing the center of the circle.)
You put your <u>right</u> foot in.
(Set right foot inside the circle.)
Your put your <u>right</u> foot out.
(Set right foot outside the circle.)
You put your <u>right</u> foot in,
(Set right foot inside the circle.)
and you shake it all about.
(Shake right foot inside circle.)
You do the hokey pokey and you turn yourself around.
(Shake your hands in the air as you take 8 small steps to turn around.)
That's what it's all about!
(Clap as you sing.)
(Repeat with "left foot...," "<u>right</u> arm..."," <u>right</u> hip...," etc.)

Special Considerations

Sincerely,

_____

SECONDARY TARGET PATTERNS: PREVOCALIC/ POSTVOCALIC SINGLETON STRIDENT

THE GINGERBREAD MAN

PATTERN

Prevocalic singleton strident

TARGET PHONEME

Word-initial /f/

TARGET WORDS

farmer, phone, finger, fan

OPENING CENTER

GOAL

To introduce word-initial /f/

MATERIALS

1. One set of alphabet letters (Appendix C)

2. Mirror

3. Pair of mittens or picture of mittens

4. Book titled *The Gingerbread Man* (1985), by Karen Lee Schmidt

PROCEDURE

1. Introduce the letter *f* in the set of alphabet letters and demonstrate correct production of /f/. Sing the "Alphabet Song" (to the tune of "Twinkle, Twinkle, Little Star") and point to the letter *f* in the set of alphabet letters. (If appropriate, also point out that the letters *ph* together make the *f* sound as in the word *phone*.)

2. Have the children produce /f/ in the mirror.

3. Introduce *The Gingerbread Man*. Talk about how the gingerbread man runs fast. Explain that the word *fast* starts with /f/. Point out the letter *f* in words such as *fast*, *farmer*, and *fox*.

4. Read *The Gingerbread Man*. Model word-initial /f/ in the words *fast*, *farmer*, *fox*, etc.

5. Say the fingerplays "The Mitten Song" and "Five Little Monkeys."

"The Mitten Song"

Thumbs in the thumb place.
(Hold both hands up and spread fingers apart; wiggle your thumbs.)
Fingers all together.
(Close your fingers together.)
This is the song we sing in mitten weather.
(Move hands back and forth in a mitten-like position.)

"Five Little Monkeys"

Five little monkeys falling off the bed.
(Hold one hand on top of the other hand and bounce hand up and down.)
One fell off and bumped his head.
(Hold your index finger up and pretend to fall off the bed.)
Mama called the doctor
(Hold your hand up to your ear.)
and the doctor said,
"No more monkeys falling off the bed."
(Point your index finger at the pretend monkeys.)

(Repeat with "four little monkeys...," holding four fingers up; "three little monkeys...," holding three fingers up; "two little monkeys...," holding two fingers up; and "one little monkey...," etc.)

No more monkeys jumping on the bed!

LISTENING CENTER

GOAL

To provide clear auditory stimuli for word-initial /f/

MATERIALS

1. One amplifier and one connector with headset per child

2. Listening list: *fast, face, feet, farm, fun, food, fall, first, find, fox*

3. Illustrations of the four target words (pages 270–271; duplicate, cut out, and staple together)

4. Play dough

5. One plastic fork per child

PROCEDURE

Optional Activity

Using the play dough and the cookie cutters, help the children cut out the letter f, feet, or fingers. Elicit /f/.

1. Instruct the children to wear their headsets and to listen. Speak into the amplifier and read the listening list to the children.

2. Introduce the four target words— *farmer, phone, finger, fan*—to the children using the illustrations.

3. Instruct the children to continue wearing their headsets as you present a model of each target word. Have the children take turns repeating each word after it has been presented to each of them.

4. Have the children roll the play dough into a ball and then press it down to make a cookie. Demonstrate how they can use a fork to make a criss-cross on top of the cookie to look like a peanut butter cookie. Elicit word-initial /f/ in the word *fork*.

PRACTICE CENTER

GOAL

To facilitate production of word-initial /f/

MATERIALS

Optional Materials

Happy face stickers

1. One printed name card per child (see page 14)

2. Illustrations of the four target words (pages 270–271; duplicate, cut out, and staple together one set per child)

3. Colored markers

4. Each child's *Remediation Data Form* (Appendix B)

5. *Family Letter* (pages 274–275; duplicate one per child)

6. One speech folder per child

PROCEDURE

1. Have the children find their own name card. Once identified, instruct the children to finger-trace and say the letters in their names.

2. Instruct the children to color the four target word illustrations—*farmer, phone, finger, fan*—using the colored markers.

3. Have the children take turns naming the target word illustrations. The goal is to elicit word-initial /f/.

4. Document the children's productions on their *Remediation Data Forms*.

5. Write notes related to each child's goal on his or her *Family Letter*.

ART CENTER

GOAL

To provide additional word-initial /f/ production practice and to create visual aids for home activities

MATERIALS

1. *Farm Animal Feet* (page 272; duplicate one per child)

2. Finger paint

3. *Face Puppets* (page 273; duplicate one per child)

4. Crayons

5. Scissors

6. Stapler

7. Four tongue depressors or popsicle sticks per child

PROCEDURE

Farm Animal Feet

1. Explain to the children they will make feet for the farm animals. Tell them to give the farm animals feet by dipping a finger in the finger paint and then making fingerprints on the paper below each animal to form the feet. Instruct each child to say word-initial /f/ in the words *foot* or *feet* with each footprint they make. Talk about the *farm* animals.

2. Allow the art page to dry, and then send it home in the child's speech folder the following session.

Face Puppets

1. Discuss feelings with the children. Have the children show a sad face, a happy face, a mad face, and an excited face.

2. Tell the children to use the crayons to color the puppet faces. Model and elicit /f/ in the word *face*.

3. Cut out the face puppets and staple each one to a tongue depressor or popsicle stick.

4. Have the children use their puppets to show you a happy face, a sad face, a mad face, and an excited face while saying *face* each time.

5. Send the puppets home in the child's speech folder.

HOME PRACTICE

GOAL

To provide home suggestions for what the children can do in the context of their everyday lives

MATERIALS

1. Each child's set of colored target word illustrations

2. Each child's completed art pages and face puppets

3. Each child's speech folder

4. Each child's *Family Letter*

PROCEDURE

1. Collect the children's colored target word illustrations, completed art page, and face puppets, and send them home in their speech folders.

2. Write any special instructions specific to a child on the *Family Letter*, on the target word illustrations, or on the art pages.

Optional Snack Activity

At the end of the session, set out gingerbread cookies. Have each child request a snack by saying, "Run, run, as fast as you can..." Elicit /f/ based on each child's skill level.

farmer

phone

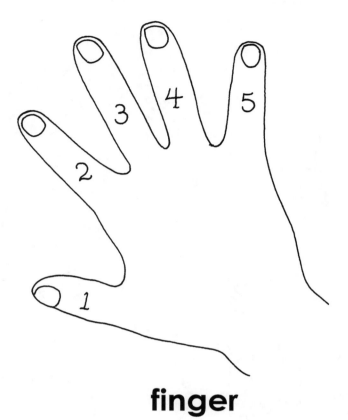

finger

fan

Talk about how you used your finger to make feet on the farm animals.

excited

sad

happy

mad

Color the face puppets. Talk about the feelings on the face puppets.

Date: _____

Dear Family,

In this lesson, the focus is on the *f* sound at the beginning of words. Young children with speech difficulties sometimes omit the "friction" feature of the *f* sound. The friction is produced when the airstream strikes the teeth forcefully. To help the children produce the *f* sound, we tell them to gently bite their bottom lip and to gently blow air.

The story for this lesson is *The Gingerbread Man,* by Karen Lee Schmidt. You'll remember this delightful story about a gingerbread man who comes to life and runs away from everyone who tries to catch him. The repetitive phrases, such as "Run, run as *fast* as you can," the *f* sounds in the words *farmer, far,* etc., and the predictability of the story offer many opportunities for listening to and saying the *f* sound.

Listening List

Read this list to your child. Slightly emphasize the *f* sound at the beginning of each word.

fast	face	feet	farm
fun	food	fall	first
find	fox		

Target Words

Using the pages in the speech folder, practice saying these words with your child. Follow the instructions provided at the end of this letter for any special considerations.

farmer	finger
phone	fan

Suggested Home Activities

1. Read the story *The Gingerbread Man* to your child. Slightly emphasize the *f* sound at the beginning of the words *fast, farmer,* and *fox.*

2. Make funny faces and talk about the faces. Have your child tell you what kind of face to make (e.g., excited face, sad face). Play with the face puppets your child brings home. Talk about the feelings each face shows.

3. Talk on the phone saying things such as, "How are you?" "I am fine." Help your child say *fine.*

4. Count fingers, toes, etc. 1–2–3–4–5. (If your child does not correctly say the *f* at the beginning of *four* or *five,* just have your child listen to you say it.)

5. Admire the *Farm Animal Feet* art page your child brings home. Talk about how his or her finger made the feet.

Fingerplays

The following fingerplays are being practiced in class. You can help your child use the *f* sound by having him or her listen as you slightly emphasize the *f* sound at the beginning of the underlined words.

"The Mitten Song"

Thumbs in the thumb place.
(Hold both hands up and spread fingers apart; wiggle your thumbs.)
<u>Fingers</u> all together.
(Close your fingers together.)
This is the song we sing in mitten weather.
(Move hands back and forth in a mitten-like position.)

"<u>Five</u> Little Monkeys"

<u>Five</u> little monkeys falling off the bed.
(Hold one hand on top of the other hand and bounce hand up and down.)
One fell off and bumped his head.
(Hold your index finger up and pretend to fall off the bed.)
Mama called the doctor
(Hold your hand up to your ear.)
and the doctor said,
"No more monkeys falling off the bed."
(Point your index finger at the pretend monkeys.)

(Repeat with "four little monkeys...," holding four fingers up; "three little monkeys...," holding three fingers up; "two little monkeys...," holding two fingers up; and "one little monkey...," etc.)

No more monkeys jumping on the bed!

Special Considerations

Sincerely,

_____

FIVE LITTLE DUCKS

PATTERN

Prevocalic singleton strident

TARGET PHONEME

Word-initial /f/

TARGET WORDS

four, five, fork, fire

OPENING CENTER

GOAL

To introduce word-initial /f/

Optional Materials

Bucket of objects such as a fish, a numeral 4, a numeral 5, a play farm, a feather, a fork, foil

MATERIALS

1. One set of alphabet letters (Appendix C)

2. Mirror

3. Facial tissue

4. Book titled *Five Little Ducks* (1989), by Raffi

Helpful Hint

For children having difficulty producing /f/, instruct them to gently bite their lower lip and blow.

PROCEDURE

1. Introduce the letter *f* in the set of alphabet letters and demonstrate correct production of /f/. Sing the "Alphabet Song" (to the tune of "Twinkle, Twinkle, Little Star") and point to the letter *f* in the set of alphabet letters.

2. Have the children produce /f/ while looking in the mirror.

3. Have the children produce /f/ while you hold the tissue in front of their mouths. Children enjoy seeing the tissue move.

4. Introduce *Five Little Ducks*. Point out the letter *f* in the title word *five*. Have the children take turns finger-tracing the letter *f* as you clearly articulate /f/ in the title word *five*.

5. Read *Five Little Ducks*. Model word-initial /f/ in the words *four, five, far*, etc.

6. Say the fingerplay "Fish Alive" and sing the song "I'm a Little Fishy."

"Fish Alive"

1-2-3-4-5,
(Hold your hands up and count with your fingers.)
once I caught a fish alive.
(Gesture catching a fish.)
6-7-8-9-10,
(Hold your hands up and count with your fingers.)
then I let him go again.
(Gesture letting the fish free from your clasped hands.)
Why did you let him go?
Because he bit my finger so.
Which finger did he bite?
This little finger on my right.
(Hold up the little finger of your right hand.)

"I'm a Little Fishy"

(Sing to the tune of "I'm a Little Teapot.")

I'm a little fishy. I can swim.
(Put your palms together and make a fish motion.)
Here is my tail. Here is my fin.
(Gesture a tail motion with your hand; then gesture a fin motion by placing your hand on your hip and waving your elbow.)
When I want to have fun with my friends,
I just wiggle my tail and jump right in!
(Use your hand to make a tail and wiggle it; then jump as you sing "jump right in.")

Optional Activity

Have the children close their eyes and reach into the bucket for an object. Model the name of the object. Label the object for the children articulating word-initial /f/. Have the children produce the word or word approximation after your model.

LISTENING CENTER

GOAL

To provide clear auditory stimuli for word-initial /f/

MATERIALS

1. One amplifier and one connector with headset per child

2. Listening list: *face, fish, farm, feather, fun, fall, full, fan, foot, fort*

3. Illustrations of the four target words (pages 281–282; duplicate, cut out, and staple together)

4. Play dough

5. One plastic fork per child

6. One miniature marshmallow per child

PROCEDURE

1. Instruct the children to wear their headsets and to listen. Speak into the amplifier and read the listening list to the children.

2. Introduce the four target words—*four, five, fork, fire*—to the children using the illustrations.

3. Instruct the children to continue wearing their headsets as you present a model of each target word. Have the children take turns repeating each word after it has been presented to each of them.

4. Have the children use the play dough to make a campfire. Instruct the children to roll four or five logs out of play dough to start the campfire. Give each child a plastic fork and a miniature marshmallow. Pretend to roast the marshmallow for four or five minutes over the fire using the fork. Elicit /f/.

PRACTICE CENTER

GOAL

To facilitate production of word-initial /f/

MATERIALS

1. One printed name card per child (see page 14)

2. Illustrations of the four target words (pages 281–282; duplicate, cut out, and staple together one set per child)

3. Colored markers

4. Each child's *Remediation Data Form* (Appendix B)

5. *Family Letter* (pages 285–286; duplicate one per child)

6. One speech folder per child

PROCEDURE

1. Have the children find their own name card. Once identified, instruct the children to finger-trace and say letters in their names.

2. Instruct the children to color the four target word illustrations—*four, five, fork, fire*—using the colored markers.

3. Have the children take turns naming the target word illustrations. The goal is to elicit word-initial /f/.

4. Document the children's productions on their *Remediation Data Forms*.

5. Write notes related to each child's goal on his or her *Family Letter.*

ART CENTER

GOAL

To provide additional word-initial /f/ production practice and to create visual aids for home activities

MATERIALS

1. *Five Ducks Having Fun* (page 283; duplicate one per child)

2. Blue watercolor paint

3. One paintbrush per child

4. Five small yellow feathers per child

5. Glue

6. *Foil Fish* (page 284; duplicate one per child)

7. Glitter crayons

8. Six small aluminum foil triangles per child

PROCEDURE

Five Ducks Having Fun

1. Have the children paint the water blue and glue the feathers on the ducks.

2. Have the children count the ducks. Model and elicit word-initial /f/ in the words *four* and *five*.

3. Allow the art page to dry, and then send it home in the child's speech folder the following session.

Foil Fish

1. Have the children color the fish scales with the glitter crayons and glue the foil triangles on the fins of the fish. Model and elicit word-initial /f/ in the word *fin* for each piece of foil the child glues on the paper.

2. Allow the art page to dry, and then send it home in the child's speech folder the following session.

Optional Snack Activity

At the end of the session, set out Pepperidge Farm Goldfish crackers. You may want to offer the children five fish crackers. Have each child request a snack by counting out the fish crackers (e.g., "May I have one fish, two fish, three fish, four fish, five fish crackers?").

HOME PRACTICE

GOAL

To provide home suggestions for what the children can do in the context of their everyday lives

MATERIALS

1. Each child's set of colored target word illustrations

2. Each child's completed art pages

3. Each child's speech folder

4. Each child's *Family Letter*

PROCEDURE

1. Collect the children's colored target word illustrations and completed art pages, and send them home in their speech folders.

2. Write any special instructions specific to a child on the *Family Letter*, on the target word illustrations, or on the art pages.

four

five

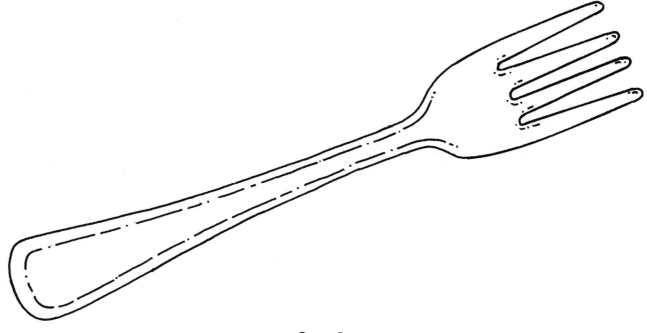

fork

fire

Five Ducks Having Fun

**Count the ducks. 1-2-3-4-5 little ducks having fun!
Talk about the feathers on the duck.**

Foil Fish

Glue the fins on the fish. Then count the fish. Talk about the fins on the five fish.

Family Letter

Date: _____

Dear Family,

In this lesson, children enjoy the book and song *Five Little Ducks*, by Raffi. While reading the book, the "friction" feature of the *f* sound at the beginning of words will be the focus. Children typically enjoy the rhyme and rhythm Raffi brings to his stories and songs. There are some great *f* words in this story for your child to practice: *four, five,* and *far away.*

Listening List

Read this list to your child. Slightly emphasize the *f* sound at the beginning of each word. Have your child listen to the friction produced by the *f* sound.

face	fish	farm	feather
fun	fall	full	fan
foot	fort		

Target Words

Using the pages in the speech folder, practice saying these words with your child. Follow the instructions provided at the end of this letter for any special considerations.

four	fork
five	fire

Suggested Home Activities

1. Read the story *Five Little Ducks* to your child. Have your child listen to the friction produced by *f* at the beginning of the words *four, five* and *far away.*

2. Pretend to be the giant in *Jack and the Beanstalk* and say, "Fe, Fi, Fo, Fum!"

3. Talk about animals that live on a farm. Slightly emphasize the word *farm.*

4. Have your child help fill glasses full of milk. (If your child does not correctly produce the *f* sound at the beginning of words after your model, only have him or her listen to you say the words correctly.)

5. Review the *Five Ducks Having Fun* art page. Help your child count the ducks and practice saying the words *four* and *five.* Admire the feathers your child added to the duck.

6. Review the *Foil Fish* art page. Talk about the *f* sound in the words *fish, foil,* and *fins.* Count the fish, helping your child say *four* and *five.*

Fingerplays and Songs

The following fingerplay and song are being practiced in class. You can help your child use the *f* sound by having him or her listen as you slightly emphasize the *f* sound at the beginning of the underlined words.

"<u>Fish</u> Alive"

1-2-3-<u>4</u>-<u>5</u>,
(Hold your hands up and count with your fingers.)
once I caught a <u>fish</u> alive.
(Gesture catching a fish.)
6-7-8-9-10,
(Hold your hands up and count with your fingers.)
then I let him go again.
(Gesture letting the fish free from your clasped hands.)
Why did you let him go?
Because he bit my <u>finger</u> so.
Which <u>finger</u> did he bite?
This little <u>finger</u> on my right.
(Hold up the little finger of your right hand.)

"I'm a Little <u>Fishy</u>"
(Sing to the tune of "I'm a Little Teapot.")

I'm a little <u>fishy</u>. I can swim.
(Put your palms together and make a fish motion.)
Here is my tail. Here is my <u>fin</u>.
(Gesture a tail motion with your hand; then gesture a fin motion by placing your hand on your hip and waving your elbow.)
When I want to have <u>fun</u> with my <u>friends</u>,
I just wiggle my tail and jump right in!
(Use your hand to make a tail and wiggle it; then jump as you sing "jump right in.")

Special Considerations

Sincerely,

_____

THE THREE LITTLE PIGS

PATTERN

Postvocalic singleton strident

TARGET PHONEME

Word-final /f/

TARGET WORDS

knife, off, roof, wolf

OPENING CENTER

GOAL

To introduce word-final /f/

MATERIALS

1. One set of alphabet letters (Appendix C)

2. Mirror

3. Book titled *The Three Little Pigs* (1973), by Elizabeth Ross

4. One set of target words

Optional Materials

Bucket of objects such as a knife, a wolf, a leaf, a scarf, a baby calf, a giraffe, a roof on a house, sandpaper to feel "rough"

PROCEDURE

1. Introduce the letter *f* in the set of alphabet letters and demonstrate correct production of /f/. Sing the "Alphabet Song" (to the tune of "Twinkle, Twinkle, Little Star") and point to the letter *f* in the set of alphabet letters.

2. Have the children produce /f/ in isolation. Provide nonsense syllable practice (e.g., /æf/, /of/, /uf/, /ɪf/).

3. Read the story *The Three Little Pigs*. Model word-final /f/ in the words *huff, puff, off, roof*, etc.

4. Say the fingerplay "Five Little Snow People" and sing the song "Down by the Station."

"Five Little Snow People"
(Similar to "Five Little Monkeys" fingerplay)

Five little snow people riding on a sled.
(Hold up five fingers and bounce to the rhythm of the rhyme.)
One fell off and off came the head.
Frosty called the doctor and the doctor said,
"No more snow people riding on the sled!"
(Shake a finger at the children.)

(Repeat with "four little snow people riding on a sled...," "three little snow people...," "two little snow people...," "one little snow person...," holding up four fingers, then three, then two, then one.)

"Down by the Station"

Down by the station, early in the morning,
see the little puffer bellies all in a row.
See the engine driver pull the little throttle.
(Pretend to pull a throttle.)
Puff! Puff! *(Pull your arm down twice.)*
Toot! Toot! *(Pretend to toot a whistle twice.)*
Off we go!

LISTENING CENTER

GOAL

To provide clear auditory stimuli for word-final /f/

MATERIALS

1. One amplifier and one connector with headset per child

2. Listening list: *huff, puff, half, leaf, scarf, gruff, beef, rough, tough, laugh*

3. Illustrations of the four target words (pages 292–293; duplicate, cut out, and staple together)

4. Play dough

5. One plastic knife per child

PROCEDURE

1. Instruct the children to wear their headsets and to listen. Speak into the amplifier and read the listening list to the children.

2. Introduce the four target words—*knife, off, roof, wolf*—to the children using the illustrations.

3. Instruct the children to continue wearing their headsets as you present a model of each target word. Have the children take turns repeating each word after it has been presented to each of them.

4. Roll the play dough and help the children cut walls and make a roof for a house using the plastic knife.

5. Make a pretend wolf and say, "Huff and puff." Have the wolf climb to the top of the house. Tell the children to say, "Get off the roof, Wolf!"

Optional Activity

Using the play dough and the cookie cutters, help the children cut out the letter f and a wolf. Elicit /f/ for the letter f and elicit word-final /f/ in the word wolf.

PRACTICE CENTER

GOAL

To facilitate production of word-final /f/

MATERIALS

1. One printed name card per child (see page 14)

2. Illustrations of the four target words (pages 292–293; duplicate, cut out, and staple together one set per child)

3. Colored markers

4. Each child's *Remediation Data Form* (Appendix B)

5. *Family Letter* (pages 296–297; duplicate one per child)

6. One speech folder per child

Optional Materials

Stickers ending with /f/ (e.g., wolf stickers)

PROCEDURE

1. Have the children find their own name card. Once identified, instruct the children to finger-trace and say the letters in their names.

2. Instruct the children to color the four target word illustrations—*knife, off, roof, wolf*—using the colored markers.

3. Have the children take turns naming the target word illustrations. The goal is to elicit word-final /f/.

4. Document the children's productions on their *Remediation Data Forms*.

5. Write notes related to each child's goal on his or her *Family Letter*.

ART CENTER

GOAL

To provide additional word-final /f/ production practice and to create visual aids for home activities

MATERIALS

1. *Huff and Puff House* (page 294; duplicate one per child)

2. Cocoa Puffs or Peanut Butter Puffs cereal; one small bowl per child

3. Glue

4. *Half and Whole* (page 295; duplicate one per child)

5. An apple or an orange to cut in half to show the children the concepts of half and whole

6. One crayon per child

PROCEDURE

Huff and Puff House

1. Put dots of glue on each child's roof.

2. As you put glue on a child's page, elicit the words *huff, puff,* and *roof*. Elicit one word per dot of glue.

3. Let the children put a (Cocoa) Puff or (Peanut Butter) Puff on each dot of glue.

4. Model the sentence "Will the wolf huff and puff and blow your house in?" Elicit word-final /f/ in the words *huff* and *puff* as appropriate per child.

5. Allow the art page to dry, and then send it home in the child's speech folder the following session.

Half and Whole

1. To help children understand the concepts *half* and *whole,* show them a whole orange and tell them it's whole. Cut the orange in half and tell them the orange is now a half part. Model word-final /f/ in the word *half.* Elicit word-final /f/ in the word *half* from each child as appropriate.

2. Tell the children to find a whole orange and a half orange on *Half and Whole*. Using the crayon, have them mark half an orange, half a sandwich, half a muffin, etc. Elicit word-final /f/ in the word *half* as appropriate per child. Tell children they may color the pictures showing half of something.

3. Send this art page home in the child's speech folder.

HOME PRACTICE

GOAL

To provide home suggestions for what the children can do in the context of their everyday lives

MATERIALS

1. Each child's set of colored target word illustrations

2. Each child's completed art pages

3. Each child's speech folder

4. Each child's *Family Letter*

PROCEDURE

1. Collect the children's colored target word illustrations and completed art pages, and send them home in their speech folders.

2. Write any special instructions specific to a child on the *Family Letter*, on the target word illustrations, or on the art pages.

Optional Snack Activity

At the end of the session, place some Cocoa Puffs or Peanut Butter Puffs on a plate for each child. Instruct the children to take off one Puff at a time and eat it like a wolf. Elicit off, puff, *and* wolf *as appropriate per individual skill level. The children can also pretend they are a wolf and "huff and puff" and blow the Puffs across the table.*

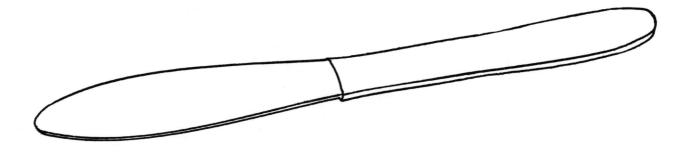

knife

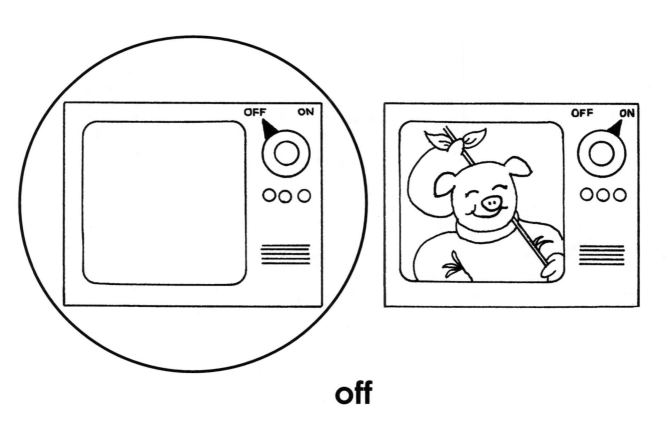

off

roof

wolf

Glue Puffs on the roof.
Will the wolf huff and puff and
blow your house in?

Half and Whole

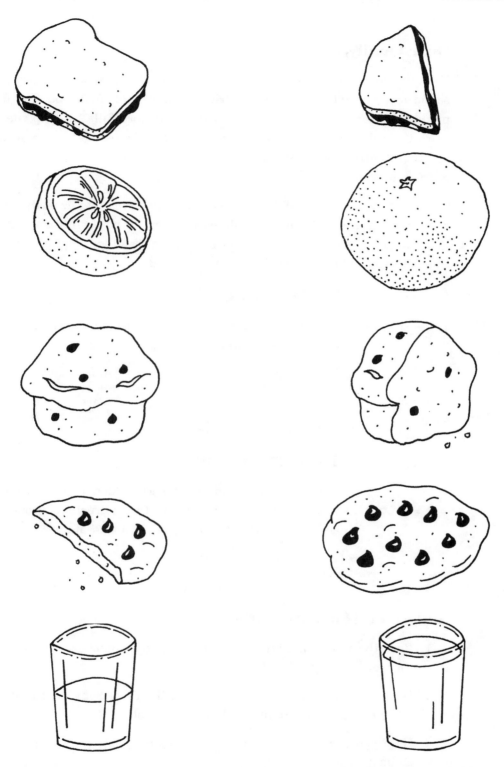

Color and talk about the pictures that show half of something.

Family Letter

Date: _____

Dear Family,

Young children whose speech is hard to understand sometimes produce the *f* sound incorrectly by omitting the "friction" feature of the sound. The friction is produced when the airstream strikes the teeth forcefully. To help the children learn to produce friction, we tell them to place their top teeth on their lower lips and then gently blow air. When the *f* sound is correctly produced, the breath gives a "friction" sound.

The well-known children's fairy tale *The Three Little Pigs*, by Elizabeth Ross, will be read in this lesson. The children will learn to say, "Then I'll huff and I'll puff and I'll blow your house in!" The wolf's idea of "huffing" and "puffing" is certain to help the children produce the friction in the /f/ sound.

LISTENING LIST

Read this list to your child. Slightly emphasize the *f* sound at the end of each word.

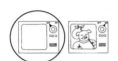

rough	tough	huff	puff
half	leaf	scarf	gruff
laugh	beef		

TARGET WORDS

Using the pages in the speech folder, practice saying these words with your child. Follow the instructions provided at the end of this letter for any special considerations.

knife	roof
off	wolf

Suggested Home Activities

1. Read the story *The Three Little Pigs*. Slightly emphasize the *f* at the end of the words *huff, puff, roof,* and *wolf*.

2. Help your child say *off* when turning off the TV or light switch, when taking off shoes, and when taking dishes off the table.

3. Help your child understand half a cookie, a half sandwich, etc. Slightly emphasize the word *half*.

4. Show your child how to cough into a tissue. Help your child say *cough*.

5. Help your child put a butter knife beside each plate at dinnertime. Have him or her say *knife* with each one they put down.

6. Admire the *Huff and Puff House* art page your child brings home. Have your child tell you how he or she made the roof.

7. Discuss the *Half and Whole* art page with your child. Help your child say the word *half* as he or she points to each half.

Fingerplays and Songs

The following fingerplay and song are being practiced in class. You can help your child use the *f* sound by having him or her listen as you slightly emphasize the *f* sound at the end of the underlined words.

"Five Little Snow People"
(Similar rhyme to "Five Little Monkeys" fingerplay)

Five little snow people riding on a sled.
(Hold up five fingers and bounce to the rhythm of the rhyme.)
One fell <u>off</u> and <u>off</u> came the head.
Frosty called the doctor and the doctor said,
"No more snow people riding on the sled!"
(Shake a finger at the children.)

(Repeat with "four little snow people riding on a sled...," "three little snow people...," "two little snow people...," "one little snow person...," holding up four fingers, then three, then two, then one.)

"Down by the Station"

Down by the station, early in the morning,
see the little puffer bellies all in a row.
See the engine driver pull the little throttle.
(Pretend to pull a throttle.)
<u>Puff</u>! <u>Puff</u>! *(Pull your arm down twice.)*
Toot! Toot! *(Pretend to toot a whistle twice.)*
<u>Off</u> we go!

Special Considerations

Sincerely,

_____

SECONDARY
TARGET PATTERNS:
PALATAL SIBILANTS

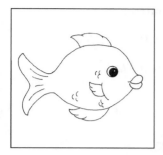

WHERE'S THE FISH?

PATTERN

Palatal sibilants

TARGET PHONEME

Word-final /ʃ/

TARGET WORDS

fish, brush, wash, push

OPENING CENTER

GOAL

To introduce word-final /ʃ/

MATERIALS

1. One set of alphabet letters (Appendix C)

2. Mirror

3. Book titled *Where's the Fish?* (1977), by Taro Gomi

PROCEDURE

1. Introduce the letters *s* and *h* in the set of alphabet letters. Demonstrate correct production of the /s/ and /h/ independently. Using the alphabet letters, tell the children that when the letters *s* and *h* stand next to each other in a word, they make one sound, /ʃ/. Sing the "Alphabet Song" (to the tune of "Twinkle, Twinkle, Little Star") and point to the letters *s* and *h* in the set of alphabet letters.

> **Optional Materials**
>
> *Bucket of objects such as a fish, a brush, a dish, a bush, a sash, a leash, cash, trash, a wash cloth*

2. Have the children produce /ʃ/ while looking in the mirror.

3. Introduce *Where's the Fish?* Point out the *sh* in the title word *fish*.

4. Read *Where's the Fish?* Model word-final /ʃ/ in the word *fish*.

5. Sing the songs "This Is the Way" and "Hush-a-Bye."

"This Is the Way"
(Add appropriate actions.)

This is the way we wash our clothes,
wash our clothes, wash our clothes.
This is the way we wash our clothes,
so early in the morning.
(Repeat the song with "This is the way we brush our teeth...," "This is the way we wash our face...," and "This is the way we brush our hair....")

"Hush-a-Bye"
(Sing to the tune of "Rock-a-Bye, Baby.")

Hush-a-bye, Baby, on the treetop.
When the wind blows, the cradle will rock.
When the bough breaks, the cradle will fall.
Down will come Baby, cradle and all.
Shhhh…

LISTENING CENTER

GOAL

To provide clear auditory stimuli for word-final /ʃ/

MATERIALS

1. One amplifier and one connector with headset per child

2. Listening list: *dish, trash, leash, mush, cash, wish, rush, dash, mash, hash*

3. Illustrations of the four target words (pages 306–307; duplicate, cut out, and staple together)

4. Play dough

5. Small toy dump truck

PROCEDURE

1. Instruct the children to wear their headsets and to listen. Speak into the amplifier and read the listening list to the children.

2. Introduce the four target words—*fish, brush, wash, push*—to the children using the illustrations.

3. Instruct the children to continue wearing their headsets as you present a model of each target word. Have the children take turns repeating each word after it has been presented to each of them.

4. Have the children roll the play dough into a ball. Then have them push the play dough with the toy truck. Model and elicit word-final /ʃ/ in the word *push*. (You could also have the children fill the truck with trash, a dish, or a fish all made from play dough.)

Optional Activity

Using the play dough and the cookie cutters, have the children cut out a fish. Elicit /ʃ/.

PRACTICE CENTER

GOAL

To facilitate production of word-final /ʃ/

MATERIALS

1. One printed name card per child (see page 14)

2. Illustrations of the four target words (pages 306–307; duplicate, cut out, and staple together one set per child)

3. Colored markers

4. Each child's *Remediation Data Form* (Appendix B)

5. *Family Letter* (pages 310–311; duplicate one per child)

6. One speech folder per child

Optional Materials

Fish stickers or other stickers ending with /ʃ/

PROCEDURE

1. Have the children find their own name card. Once identified, instruct the children to finger-trace and say the letters in their names.

2. Instruct the children to color the four target word illustrations—*fish, brush, wash, push*—using the colored markers.

3. Have the children take turns naming the target word illustrations. The goal is to elicit word-final /ʃ/.

Optional Activity

Have the children choose a fish sticker to put on their folders then ask "What is this?"

4. Document the children's productions on their *Remediation Data Forms*.

5. Write notes related to each child's goal on his or her *Family Letter*.

ART CENTER

GOAL

To provide additional word-final /ʃ/ practice and to create visual aids for home activities

MATERIALS

1. *Fish Scales* (page 308; duplicate one per child)

2. Pink paint (Mix a little red paint with white powder paint. This creates an excellent consistency for holding the salt that will be sprinkled on by the children.)

3. One paintbrush per child

4. Salt

5. *Where's the Fish?* (page 309; duplicate one per child)

6. One pink crayon per child (or pink glitter crayon)

PROCEDURE

Fish Scales

1. Have the children paint the fish pink. Elicit the word *fish* from each child as he or she paints the fish.

2. Sprinkle salt on the fish to give it a scaly effect. When the fish is dry, tell the children to feel the fish.

3. Allow the art page to dry, and then send it home in the child's speech folder the following session.

Where's the Fish?

1. Instruct the children that they need to find all the fish on the page. Elicit word-final /ʃ/ in the word *fish*. Have the children color the fish pink.

2. Elicit the /ʃ/ in the word *fish* with each child as they find each fish.

3. Send this art page home in the child's speech folder.

HOME PRACTICE

GOAL

To provide home suggestions for what the children can do in the context of their everyday lives

MATERIALS

1. Each child's set of colored target word illustrations

2. Each child's completed art pages

3. Each child's speech folder

4. Each child's *Family Letter*

PROCEDURE

1. Collect the children's colored target word illustrations and completed art pages, and then send them home in their speech folders.

2. Write any special instructions specific to a child on the *Family Letter*, on the target word illustrations, or on the art pages.

Optional Snack Activity

At the end of the session, set out Pepperidge Farm goldfish crackers. Have each child request a snack using a production based on his or her skill level.

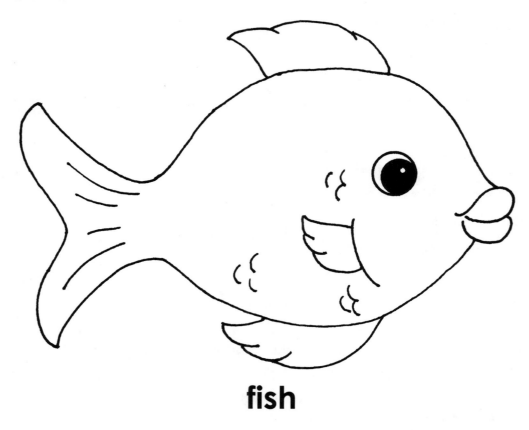

fish

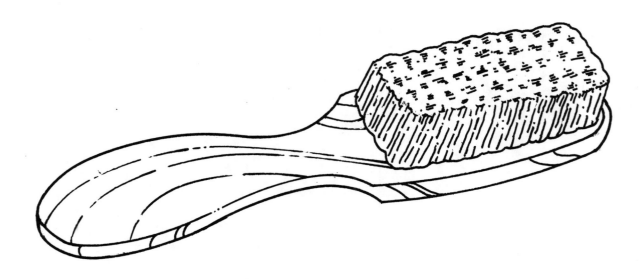

brush

wash

push

Fish Scales

Sprinkle salt on the fish. Feel the fish. Practice saying "fish."

Where's the Fish?

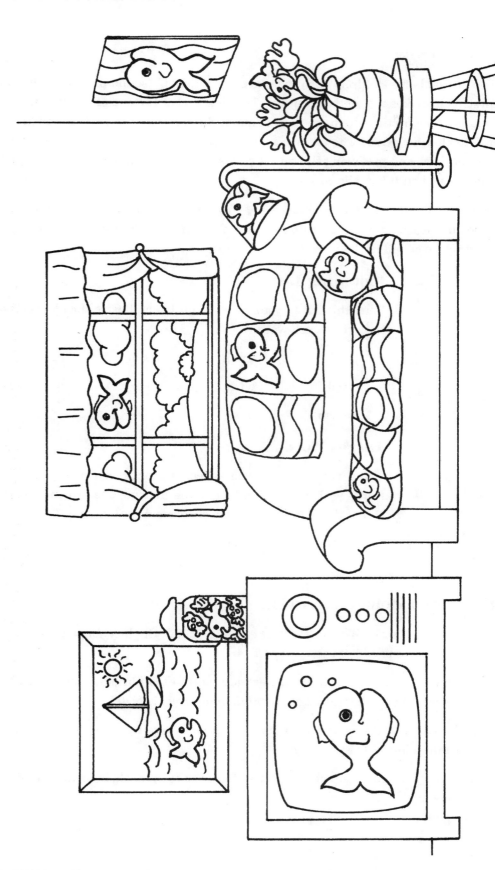

Find and color the fish.

Practice saying "fish" as you find them.

309

Family Letter

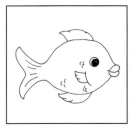

Date: _____

Dear Family,

This lesson helps children learn the concept of "friction" (sound produced when an airstream strikes the teeth forcefully). The *sh* sound at the end of words is used to help produce friction. To make the *sh* sound, children learn to protrude their lips and to blow air gently. The teeth are slightly separated. Hearing the words in the listening list and producing the target words helps children learn how *sh* sounds and feels when it is made correctly.

The book for this lesson is *Where's the Fish?* by Taro Gomi. It provides many opportunities for the children to hear the friction feature of *sh* and to practice making the sound in the word *fish*.

Listening List

Read this list to your child. Slightly emphasize the *sh* sound at the end of each word.

dish	trash	leash	mush
cash	wish	rush	dash
mash	hash		

Target Words

Using the pages in the speech folder, practice saying these words with your child. Follow the instructions provided at the end of this letter for any special considerations.

fish	wash
push	brush

Suggested Home Activities

1. Read the story *Where's the Fish?* to your child. Slightly emphasize the *sh* sound at the end of the word *fish*.

2. Have your child brush his or her teeth with a toothbrush. Have your child repeat the words *brush* and *toothbrush* after your model.

3. Play with and talk about things you can push (e.g., toy cars, shopping carts, chairs). Model the word *push*.

4. Have your child help you mash potatoes. For each mash, help your child say *mash*.

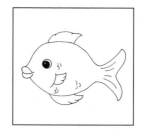

5. Help your child wash a doll in soapy water in the sink. Wash the face, hands, toes, etc. Slightly emphasize the word *wash* while washing the doll.

6. Admire the *Fish Scales* art page. Tell your child to feel the fish and then say *fish*.

7. Review *Where's the Fish?* art page. Tell your child to find each fish and say *fish* each time he or she finds one.

Songs

The following songs are being sung in class. You can help your child use the *sh* sound by having him or her listen as you slightly emphasize the *sh* sound at the end of the underlined words.

"This Is the Way"

(Add appropriate actions.)

This is the way we <u>wash</u> our clothes,
<u>wash</u> our clothes, <u>wash</u> our clothes.
This is the way we <u>wash</u> our clothes,
so early in the morning.
(Repeat the song with "This is the way we <u>brush</u> our teeth...," "This is the way we <u>wash</u> our face...," and "This is the way we <u>brush</u> our hair....")

"Hush-a-Bye"

(Sing to the tune of "Rock-a-Bye, Baby.")

<u>Hush</u>-a-bye, Baby, on the treetop.
When the wind blows, the cradle will rock.
When the bough breaks, the cradle will fall.
Down will come Baby, cradle and all.
Shhh...

Special Considerations

Sincerely,

CHICKA CHICKA BOOM BOOM

PATTERN

Palatal sibilants

TARGET SOUND

Word-initial /tʃ/

TARGET WORDS

chick, choo choo, cheese, chair

OPENING CENTER

GOAL

To introduce word-initial /tʃ/

MATERIALS

1. One set of alphabet letters (Appendix C)

2. Mirror

3. Book titled *Chicka Chicka Boom Boom* (1989), by Bill Martin Jr. and John Archambault

Optional Materials
Bucket of objects such as a chick, cheese, a chair, a choo-choo train, potato chips, chalk, a cherry, a child doll

PROCEDURE

1. Introduce the letters *c* and *h* in the set of alphabet letters and demonstrate correct production of /c/ and /h/ independently. Tell the children that when the letters *c* and *h* stand next to each other in a word, they make one sound /tʃ/. Sing the "Alphabet Song" (to the tune of "Twinkle, Twinkle, Little Star") and point to the letters *c* and *h* in the set of alphabet letters.

2. Have the children produce /tʃ/ while looking in the mirror.

3. Introduce *Chicka Chicka Boom Boom*. Point out *ch* in the title word *Chicka*.

4. Read *Chicka Chicka Boom Boom*. Model word-initial /tʃ/ in the word *Chicka*.

5. Sing the songs "Choo-Choo" and "Little Train."

"Choo-Choo"

Choo choo choo choo.
Choo choo, choo choo, goin' down the track.
Choo choo choo choo.
Choo choo, choo choo, then it comes right back.
(Move your arms back and forth like a train.)

"Little Train"

Choo choo choo choo. Choo choo choo choo.
Hurry little puffer train, cried all the children.
See our merry flags are waving to and fro.
Now when the station master blows his shiny whistle,
choo choo choo choo, off we'll go.

LISTENING CENTER

GOAL

To provide clear auditory stimuli for word-initial /tʃ/

MATERIALS

1. One amplifier and one connector with headset per child

2. Listening list: *child, chicken, chip, chain, chalk, cheek, cherry, cheat, cheap, chop*

3. Illustrations of the four target words (pages 317–318; duplicate, cut out, and staple together)

4. Play dough

> **Helpful Hint**
>
> *For children having difficulty producing /tʃ/, it is often helpful to teach them to make /tʃ/ in the word* choo choo *with an elevated pitch. This acoustic effect often helps the children make the sound more easily.*

> **Optional Activity**
>
> *Have the children close their eyes and reach into the bucket for an object. Model the name of the object, articulating word-initial /tʃ/. Have the children produce the word or word approximation after your model.*

> **Optional Materials**
>
> *Cookie cutters shaped like the letters* c *and* h

PROCEDURE

1. Instruct the children to wear their headsets and to listen. Speak into the amplifier and read the listening list to the children.

2. Introduce the four target words—*chick, choo choo, cheese, chair*—to the children using the illustrations.

3. Instruct the children to continue wearing their headsets as you present a model of each target word. Have the children take turns repeating each word after it has been presented to each of them.

4. Make a play dough mouse. Help the children make a chunk of cheese. Have the mouse chew each child's cheese. Elicit the words *chunk, cheese,* and *chew* from each child.

PRACTICE CENTER

GOAL

To facilitate production of word-initial /tʃ/

MATERIALS

1. One printed name card per child (see page 14)

2. Illustrations of the four target words (pages 317–318; duplicate, cut out, and staple together one set per child)

3. Colored markers

4. Each child's *Remediation Data Form* (Appendix B)

5. *Family Letter* (pages 321–322; duplicate one per child)

6. One speech folder per child

PROCEDURE

1. Have the children find their own name card. Once identified, instruct the children to finger-trace and say the letters in their names.

2. Have the children color the four target illustrations—*chick, choo choo, cheese, chair*—using the colored markers.

3. Have the children take turns naming the target word illustrations. The goal is to elicit word-initial /tʃ/.

4. Document the children's productions on their *Remediation Data Forms*.

5. Write notes related to each child's goal on his or her *Family Letter*.

ART CENTER

GOAL

To provide additional word-initial /tʃ/ production practice and to create visual aids for home activities

MATERIALS

1. *Chicky Chick* (page 319; duplicate one per child)

2. Yellow tissue paper cut into small squares, approximately 2 x 2"

3. Glue

4. *Chewy Cereal from the Chicka Tree* (page 320; duplicate one per child)

5. Chalk in a variety of colors

6. Alpha-Bits cereal

PROCEDURE

Chicky Chick

1. Tell the children to crunch the yellow tissue paper squares.

2. Help the children glue on the crunched tissue paper pieces as the chick's feathers. Elicit word-initial /tʃ/ in the word *chick* each time a child glues a feather on the chick.

3. Allow the art page to dry, and then send it home in the child's speech folder the following session.

Chewy Cereal from the Chicka Tree

1. Help the children color the coconut tree and the letters with different colors of chalk. Elicit word-initial /tʃ/ in the word *chalk*.

2. Give each child a handful of Alpha-Bits cereal. If possible, give each child a letter *c* and a letter *h* from the cereal.

3. Using the glue, help the children put on their page as many dots of glue as they have pieces of cereal.

4. Using the letters *c* and *h*, show the children how to place the little bits of cereal on the glue. Model /tʃ/ after the *ch* letter combination is glued on.

5. Tell the children to place the remaining bits of cereal on the remaining dots of glue.

6. Explain to the children that each one of the bits of cereal is a letter, and that each of the letters makes a different sound. When you put certain letters together, they make certain sounds called *words*.

7. If possible, demonstrate how letters make words using the bits of cereal. Try to make words beginning with /tʃ/. Model and elicit word-initial /tʃ/ in the words created.

8. This may be a good time to offer each child a small snack. After each child creates a word beginning with /tʃ/, tell him or her to "chew" and/or "chomp" the *ch* word up!

9. Allow the art page to dry, and then send it home in the child's speech folder the following session.

Optional Snack Activity
During the art center, set out a snack beginning with /tʃ/ (e.g., chips, cheese, or chocolate chip [cookies]). Have each child request a snack using a production based on his or her skill level.

HOME PRACTICE

GOAL

To provide home suggestions for what the children can do in the context of their everyday lives

MATERIALS

1. Each child's set of colored target word illustrations

2. Each child's completed art pages

3. Each child's speech folder

4. Each child's *Family Letter*

PROCEDURE

1. Collect the children's colored target word illustrations and completed art pages, and then send them home in their speech folders.

2. Write any special instructions specific to a child on the *Family Letter*, on the target word illustrations, or on the art pages.

chick

choo choo

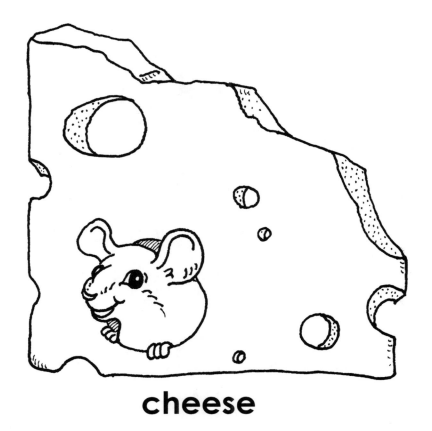

cheese

chair

Chicky Chick

Crunch and paste
yellow tissue paper on the chick.
Say "chick" as you paste.

Chewy Cereal from the Chicka Tree

After you color with chalk, glue on the chewy cereal. Practice saying "chalk" and "chew."

Family Letter

Date: _____

Dear Family,

In this lesson, children will learn how to produce the *ch* sound at the beginning of words. The *ch* sound is introduced with the book *Chicka Chicka Boom Boom,* by Bill Martin Jr. and John Archambault. This is a lively, sort of "jazzy" alphabet book. There is frequent repetition of the phrase *Chicka Chicka Boom Boom* so the children have many opportunities to hear the *ch* sound and to practice saying it. Children usually find the rhythm and beat of the story to be fun. Children are exposed to the alphabet which will promote readiness for school.

Children will learn to make the *ch* sound in the word *choo choo* using an elevated pitch. This acoustic effect often helps children make the sound more easily. The children will also be asked be reminded that *ch* makes an "explosion of sound."

Listening List

Read this list to your child. Slightly emphasize the *ch* sound at the beginning of each word.

child	chicken	chip	chain
chalk	cheek	cherry	cheat
cheap	chop		

Target Words

Using the pages in the speech folder, practice saying these words with your child. Follow the instructions provided at the end of this letter for any special considerations.

chick	cheese
chair	choo choo

Suggested Home Activities

1. Read the story *Chicka Chicka Boom Boom* to your child. Slightly emphasize the *ch* sound at the beginning of the word *chicka*.

2. Talk about chewy food, chopping vegetables, and eating cheese pizza. Model the words *chewy, chopping,* and *cheese.*

3. Make macaroni and cheese. Add the cheese a small bit at a time, saying the word *cheese* each time you add a bit.

4. Identify body parts including your child's and your cheek and chin. Help your child say the words *cheek* and *chin.*

5. Bake chocolate chip cookies. Then help your child say the words *chocolate* and *chip*.

6. Review the *Chicky Chick* art page. Talk about the *chick*, the yellow *chick*, the little *chick*.

7. Review the *Chewy Cereal from the Chicka Tree* art page. Help your child say the words *chalk* and *chew*.

Songs

The following songs are being practiced in class. You can help your child use the *ch* sound by having him or her listen as you slightly emphasize the *ch* sound at the beginning of the underlined words.

"Choo-Choo"

<u>Choo</u> <u>choo</u> <u>choo</u> <u>choo</u>.
<u>Choo</u> <u>choo</u>, <u>choo</u> <u>choo</u>, goin' down the track.
<u>Choo</u> <u>choo</u> <u>choo</u> <u>choo</u>.
<u>Choo</u> <u>choo</u>, <u>choo</u> <u>choo</u>, then it comes right back.
(Move your arms back and forth like a train.)

"Little Train"

<u>Choo</u> <u>choo</u> <u>choo</u> <u>choo</u>. <u>Choo</u> <u>choo</u> <u>choo</u> <u>choo</u>.
Hurry little puffer train, cried all the <u>children</u>.
See our merry flags are waving to and fro.
Now when the station master blows his shiny whistle,
<u>choo</u> <u>choo</u> <u>choo</u> <u>choo</u>, off we'll go.

Special Considerations

Sincerely,

_____

SHEEP IN A SHOP

PATTERN

Palatal sibilants

TARGET PHONEME

Word-initial /ʃ/

TARGET WORDS

sheep, shy, shoe, shirt

OPENING CENTER

GOAL

To introduce word-initial /ʃ/

MATERIALS

1. One set of alphabet letters (Appendix C)

2. Mirror

3. Book titled *Sheep in a Shop* (1991), by Nancy Shaw

Optional Materials

Bucket of objects such as a shoe, a shirt, a sheep, a shell, a shark, shampoo, a toy shovel

PROCEDURE

1. Introduce the letters *s* and *h* in the set of alphabet letters and demonstrate correct production of /s/ and /h/ independently. Using the alphabet letters, tell the children that when the letters *s* and *h* stand next to each other in a word, they make one sound /ʃ/. Sing the "Alphabet Song" (to the tune of "Twinkle, Twinkle, Little Star") and point to the letters *s* and *h* in the set of alphabet letters.

323

2. Tell the children to pretend there is a baby sleeping in the room. Have the children hold their index finger to their lips and produce /ʃ/.

3. Introduce *Sheep in a Shop.* Point out *sh* in the title words *sheep* and *shop.*

4. Read *Sheep in a Shop.* Model word-initial /ʃ/ in the words *sheep* and *shop.*

5. Sing the song "Five Sheep in a Shop," and say the rhyme "One, Two, Buckle My Shoe."

"Five Sheep in a Shop"
(Sing to the tune of "I Saw Three Ships Go Sailing In.")

I saw five sheep go in a shop,
go in a shop, go in a shop.
I saw five sheep go in a shop.
We'll see what they can swap.

A ball and ribbon are what they want,
are what they want, are what they want.
A ball and ribbon are what they want
to buy, the sheep in a shop.

"One, Two, Buckle My Shoe"

One, two, buckle my shoe.
(Pretend to buckle your shoe.)
Three, four, shut the door.
(Pretend to shut a door.)
Five, six, pick up sticks.
(Pretend to pick up sticks.)
Seven, eight, lay them straight.
(Pretend to lay them down in a straight line.)
Nine, ten, a big fat hen.
(Extend your arms out from your stomach in a big circle.)

LISTENING CENTER

GOAL

To provide clear auditory stimuli for word-initial/ʃ/

MATERIALS

1. One amplifier and one connector with headset per child

2. Listening list: *sheep, shelf, shout, shy, shine, shucks, shut, ship, shovel, shave*

3. Illustrations of the four target words (pages 328–329; duplicate, cut out, and staple together)

4. Play dough

5. One can of shaving cream

PROCEDURE

1. Instruct the children to wear their headsets and to listen. Speak into the amplifier and read the listening list to the children.

2. Introduce the four target words—*sheep, shy, shoe, shirt*—to the children using the illustrations.

3. Instruct the children to continue wearing their headsets as you present a model of each target word. Have the children take turns repeating each word after it has been presented to each of them.

4. Using play dough, help the children form a letter *s* and a letter *h*. Model /ʃ/. Instruct the children to imitate /ʃ/.

5. Spray a small amount of the shaving cream in front of each child. Instruct the children to flatten and spread out the shaving cream in front of them. Have the children practice drawing the *sh* combination in the shaving cream. Elicit the sound productions as each child draws the combination with his or her finger.

PRACTICE CENTER

GOAL

To facilitate production of word-initial /ʃ/

MATERIALS

1. One printed name card per child (see page 14)

2. Illustrations of the four target words (pages 328–329; duplicate, cut out, and staple together one set per child)

3. Colored markers

4. Each child's *Remediation Data Form* (Appendix B)

5. *Family Letter* (pages 332–333; duplicate one per child)

Optional Materials

1. *Cookie cutters shaped like a shamrock, a shoe, a shirt, or the letters s and h*

2. *One miniature toy sheep per child*

Optional Activities

1. *Using the play dough and the cookie cutters, help the children cut out shamrocks, shoes, shirts, or the letters s and h. Elicit the appropriate /ʃ/ responses from each child based on his or her skill level.*

2. *Have each child make a pretend fenced yard with a gate using the play dough. Give each child a toy sheep to put inside the fence and shut the gate. Elicit the words* sheep *and* shut *from each child.*

Optional Materials

Stickers beginning with /ʃ/ (e.g., sheep, ship, or shoe stickers)

6. One speech folder per child

PROCEDURE

Optional Activity

Have the children choose a sticker to put on their speech folders. Then talk or ask questions about the sticker to elicit word-initial /ʃ/ productions (e.g., "What animal says 'baa'?" to elicit "Sheep").

1. Have the children find their own name card. Once identified, instruct the children to finger-trace and say the letters in their names.

2. Instruct the children to color the four target word illustrations—*sheep, shy, shoe, shirt*—using the colored markers.

3. Have the children take turns naming the target word illustrations. The goal is to elicit word-initial /ʃ/.

4. Document the children's productions on their *Remediation Data Forms*.

5. Write notes related to each child's goal on his or her *Family Letter*.

ART CENTER

GOAL

To provide additional word-initial /ʃ/ production practice and to create visual aids for home activities

MATERIALS

1. *Hidden Shoes in a Shop* (page 330; duplicate one per child)

2. One colored pencil per child (any color)

3. *Sheep Shapes* (page 331; duplicate one per child)

PROCEDURE

Hidden Shoes in a Shop

1. Explain to the children that there are shoes hiding in the shop.

2. Have one child find a shoe. Then tell all the children to use their colored pencil to color in the shoe on their pages. Elicit the word *shoe* from each child. Let another child find another shoe and follow the same procedure.

3. Help the children count the shoes that were hiding.

4. Send this art page home in the child's speech folder.

Sheep Shapes

1. Explain to the children that there are shapes on each sheep in the left-hand column that match the shapes on each sheep in the right-hand column, while pointing to the respective column.

2. Point to the sheep in the left-hand column with a heart. Then point to the sheep in the right-hand column with a heart.

3. Have the children use their colored pencil to draw a line connecting the two sheep.

4. Have the children draw lines matching sheep with the same shapes. Have them say the words *sheep* and *shape* as they draw.

HOME PRACTICE

GOAL

To provide home suggestions for what the children can do in the context of their everyday lives

MATERIALS

1. Each child's set of colored target word illustrations

2. Each child's completed art pages

3. Each child's speech folder

4. Each child's *Family Letter*

PROCEDURE

1. Collect the children's colored target word illustrations and completed art pages, and then send them home in their speech folders.

2. Write any special instructions specific to a child on the *Family Letter*, on the target word illustrations, or on the art pages.

Optional Snack Activity

At the end of the session, set out shark Fruit Roll-ups or shortbread cookies. Have each child request a snack using a production based on his or her skill level.

sheep

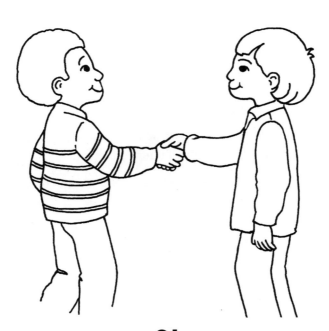

Shy—
They are not shy.

shoe

shirt

Find the shoes in the shop.
Say "shoe" each time you find
a hidden shoe. Then count the shoes.

Sheep Shapes

Draw a line to connect
the matching shapes on the sheep.
What shapes are on the sheep?

Family Letter

Date: _____

Dear Family,

This lesson focuses on the *sh* sound at the beginning of words. The *sh* sound is a continuous airflow with some friction created by the air stream striking the teeth forcefully. Additionally, the front part of the tongue is raised and placed against the side teeth and gums, the lips are protruded a little, and the teeth are slightly separated. We ask the children to protrude their lips and blow air gently. The *sh* is referred to as the "quiet" sound. We have the children pretend there is a baby sleeping in the room, while they make the *sh* sound.

This lesson's book is a charming children's story by Nancy Shaw called *Sheep in a Shop*.

Listening List

Read this list to your child. Slightly emphasize the *sh* sound at the beginning of each word.

sheep	shelf	shout	shy
shine	shucks	shut	ship
shovel	shave		

Target Words

Using the pages in the speech folder, practice saying these words with your child. Follow the instructions provided at the end of this letter for any special considerations.

sheep	shoe
shy	shirt

Suggested Home Activities

1. Read the story *Sheep in a Shop* to your child. Slightly emphasize the *sh* sound at the beginning of the words *sheep* and *shop*.

2. When you go shopping, provide practice for the *sh* sound. (You may see sugar, shoes, shirts, etc.)

3. When you open and shut doors, have your child say the *sh* sound in *shut*.

4. Talk about different shapes. Help your child say the word *shape*.

5. Use the word *shake* for shaking salt on popcorn. Have your child repeat the word as you make the motion.

6. Review the *Hidden Shoes in a Shop* art page. Help your child count the shoes that are hiding. Have your child say the word *shoe* when counting (e.g., one *shoe*, two *shoes*, etc.).

7. Review the *Sheep Shapes* art page. Talk about the different shapes. Practice saying the *sh* in the words *sheep* and *shape*.

Songs and Rhymes

The following song and rhyme are being practiced in class. You can help your child use the *sh* sound by having him or her listen as you slightly emphasize the *sh* sound at the beginning of the underlined words.

"Five <u>Sheep</u> in a <u>Shop</u>"
(Sing to the tune of "I Saw Three Ships Go Sailing In.")

I saw five <u>sheep</u> go in a <u>shop</u>,
go in a <u>shop</u>, go in a <u>shop</u>.
I saw five <u>sheep</u> go in a <u>shop</u>.
We'll see what they can swap.

A ball and ribbon are what they want,
are what they want, are what they want.
A ball and ribbon are what they want
to buy, the <u>sheep</u> in a <u>shop</u>.

"One, Two, Buckle My <u>Shoe</u>"

One, two, buckle my <u>shoe</u>.
(Pretend to buckle your shoe.)
Three, four, <u>shut</u> the door.
(Pretend to shut a door.)
Five, six, pick up sticks.
(Pretend to pick up sticks.)
Seven, eight, lay them straight.
(Pretend to lay them down in a straight line.)
Nine, ten, a big fat hen.
(Extend your arms out from your stomach in a big circle.)

Special Considerations

Sincerely,

_____

JUMP, FROG, JUMP!

PATTERN

Palatal sibilant

TARGET PHONEME

Word-initial /ʤ/

TARGET WORDS

jump, jog, jelly, juice

OPENING CENTER

GOAL

To introduce word-initial /ʤ/

MATERIALS

> **Optional Materials**
>
> *Bucket of objects such as a jeep, a jack, a jet, a jewel, jeans, a jar of jelly, a can of juice*

1. One set of alphabet letters (Appendix C)
2. Book titled *Jump, Frog, Jump!* (1995), by Robert Kalan

PROCEDURE

1. Introduce the letter *j* in the set of alphabet letters and demonstrate correct production of /ʤ/. Sing the "Alphabet Song" (to the tune of "Twinkle, Twinkle, Little Star") and point to the letter *j* in the set of alphabet letters.

2. Pretend to start a jeep. Instruct the children to pretend to turn a key in the ignition, put their hands on the steering wheel, and put their foot on the gas pedal. Model word-initial /ʤ/ in succession while pretending to pump the gas to get the jeep started.

3. Introduce *Jump, Frog, Jump!* Point out the letter *j* in the title word *jump.*

4. Read *Jump, Frog, Jump!* Model word-initial /ʤ/ in the word *jump.*

5. Say the rhyme "Jack Be Nimble" and the fingerplay "Two Little Blackbirds."

"Jack Be Nimble"

Jack be nimble.
Jack be quick.
Jack jump over the candlestick.
Jill be nimble, and jump it too.
If Jack can jump it, Jill can too!

"Two Little Blackbirds"

Two little blackbirds sitting on a hill.
(Hold up your index finger on each hand.)
One named Jack.
(Wiggle one finger.)
One named Jill.
(Wiggle the other finger.)
Fly away Jack.
(Whisk one hand behind your back.)
Fly away Jill.
(Whisk the other hand behind your back.)
Come back Jack.
(Have one finger come back.)
Come back Jill.
(Have the other finger come back.)

LISTENING CENTER

GOAL

To provide a clear auditory stimuli for word-initial /ʤ/

MATERIALS

1. One amplifier and one connector with headset per child

2. Listening list: *jaw, jet, jazz, June, judge, gym, job, jail, joke, giant*

Helpful Hints

There are two movements involved when making /ʤ/. One movement consists of momentarily stopping the sound. The second movement is an explosive voiced release. Think of /ʤ/ as being composed of /d/ and /ʒ/, but produced in such rapid succession that the result is only one production of the two sounds. Children with phonological disorders often omit the second movement of the /ʤ/ (i.e., the "stridency" component).

Optional Activity

Have the children close their eyes and reach into the bucket for an object. Model the name of the object articulating word-initial /ʤ/. Have the children produce the word or word approximation after your model.

Optional Materials

Cookie cutters shaped like a frog for "jump" and like the letter j

3. Illustrations of the four target words (pages 339–340; duplicate, cut out, and staple together)

4. Play dough

PROCEDURE

1. Instruct the children to wear their headsets and to listen. Speak into the amplifier and read the listening list to the children.

2. Introduce the four target words—*jump, jog, jelly, juice*—to the children using the illustrations.

3. Instruct the children to continue wearing their headsets as you present a model of each target word. Have the children take turns repeating each word after it has been presented to each of them.

4. Have the children make a pretend jelly sandwich with the play dough.

PRACTICE CENTER

GOAL

To facilitate production of word-initial /ʤ/

MATERIALS

1. One printed name card per child (see page 14)

2. Illustrations of the four target words (pages 339–340; duplicate, cut out, and staple together one set per child)

3. Colored markers

4. Each child's *Remediation Data Form* (Appendix B)

5. *Family Letter* (pages 343–344; duplicate one per child)

6. One speech folder per child

PROCEDURE

1. Have the children find their own name card. Once identified, instruct the children to finger-trace and say the letters in their names.

2. Have the children color the four target word illustrations—*jump, jog, jelly, juice*—using the colored markers.

Optional Activities

Using the play dough and the frog cookie cutter, tell the children to make a pretend frog. Instruct the children to pretend the frog will "jump" in "gym" class. Elicit the words jump *and* gym. *Then use the* j *cookie cutter to make the letter* j. *Model and elicit /ʤ/.*

Optional Materials

Stickers beginning with word-initial /ʤ/ (e.g., frog stickers for "jump" or jellybean stickers)

Optional Activity

Have the children choose a sticker to put on their folders. Then talk or ask questions about the sticker to elicit word-initial /ʤ/ productions (e.g., "You chose a frog sticker. Frogs like to ___" to elicit "Jump").

3. Have the children take turns naming the target word illustrations. The goal is to elicit word-initial /ʤ/.

4. Document the children's productions on their *Remediation Data Forms*.

5. Write notes related to each child's goal on his or her *Family Letter*.

ART CENTER

GOAL

To provide additional /ʤ/ production practice and to create visual aids for home activities

MATERIALS

1. *Fruit Juice* (page 341; duplicate one per child)

2. Four bowls

3. Glue

4. Food coloring (red, yellow, blue; mix food coloring to make orange and purple)

5. Several cotton swabs per bowl

6. *Jump, Jump!* (page 342; duplicate one per child)

7. Green watercolor paint

8. One paintbrush per child

PROCEDURE

Fruit Juice

1. Before the session, add food coloring to the glue to make four glue mixtures (red, yellow, orange, purple). Put the mixtures in four separate bowls.

2. Have the children guess the name of the fruit. Tell them juice can be made from the fruit. Write the name of the fruit on the line by each drawing.

3. Have the children use a cotton swab to paint the fruit (e.g., orange for the orange, purple for the grapes).

4. Model and elicit word-initial /ʤ/ in the word *juice* as the children paint.

5. Allow the art page to dry, and then send it home in the child's speech folder the following session.

Jump, Jump!

1. Have the children use the green watercolor paint to paint the spots on the frog green.

2. Model word-initial /ʤ/ in the word *jump* as the children paint.

3. Elicit word-initial /ʤ/ in the word *jump* with each child.

4. Allow the art page to dry, and then send it home in the child's speech folder the following session.

Optional Snack

At the end of the session, set out a snack beginning with /ʤ/ (e.g., Jello Jigglers, jelly sandwiches, jellybeans, or fruit juice). Have each child request a snack using a production based on his or her skill level.

HOME PRACTICE

GOAL

To provide home suggestions for what the children can do in the context of their everyday lives

MATERIALS

1. Each child's set of colored target word illustrations

2. Each child's completed art pages

3. Each child's speech folder

4. Each child's *Family Letter*

PROCEDURE

1. Collect the children's colored target word illustrations and completed art pages, and send them home in their speech folders.

2. Write any special instructions specific to a child on the *Family Letter*, on the target word illustrations, or on the art pages.

jump

jog

jelly

juice

Fruit Juice

_____ juice

_____ juice

_____ juice

_____ juice

_____ juice

Paint the fruit.
What kind of juice can these fruits make?

341

**Paint the spots on the frog green.
Say "Jump, jump!" after you
paint each spot.**

Family Letter

Date: _____

Dear Family,

The focus of this lesson is on producing *j* at the beginning of words. There are two movements involved when making the *j* sound. The *j* sound combines a *d* sound with a *zh* sound. The two sounds are said rapidly to produce the *j* sound. Children with speech difficulty often omit the second movement of the *j* sound.

The book *Jump, Frog, Jump!* by Robert Kalan will be used to emphasize the *j* sound. In this story, the question, "How did the frog get away?" is repeatedly asked. The answer is "Jump, frog, jump!" The book offers many opportunities for children to practice the sound in the phrase "Jump, frog, jump!" Children love telling the frog "Jump, frog, jump!" in unison.

Listening List

Read this list to your child. Slightly emphasize the *j* sound at the beginning of each word.

jaw	jet	jazz	June
judge	gym	job	jail
joke	giant		

Target Words

Using the pages in the speech folder, practice saying these words with your child. Follow the instructions provided at the end of this letter for any special considerations.

jump	jog
juice	jelly

Suggested Home Activities

1. Read the story *Jump, Frog, Jump!* Slightly emphasize the *j* sound at the beginning of the word *jump*.

2. Dance to jazzy music! Ask your child if he or she likes the jazzy music, emphasizing the word *jazzy*.

3. Make orange juice with your child. Help them request the orange juice by saying *juice*.

4. See how everyone in the family can jump or jump rope. Have your child say the word *jump* each time they jump.

5. Review the *Fruit Juice* art page. Talk about each type of juice the fruit makes. Help your child say the *j* in *juice*.

6. Admire the *Jump, Jump!* art page. Point to each spot on the frog and have your child make the *j* sound. Help your child say the *j* in *"Jump, frog!"*

Rhymes and Fingerplays

The following rhyme and fingerplay are being practiced in class. You can help your child use the *j* sound by having him or her listen as you slightly emphasize the *j* sound at the beginning of the underlined words.

"<u>Jack</u> Be Nimble"

<u>Jack</u> be nimble.
<u>Jack</u> be quick.
<u>Jack</u> <u>jump</u> over the candlestick.
<u>Jill</u> be nimble, and <u>jump</u> it too.
If <u>Jack</u> can <u>jump</u> it, <u>Jill</u> can too!

"Two Little Blackbirds"

Two little blackbirds sitting on a hill.
(Hold up your index finger on each hand.)
One named <u>Jack</u>.
(Wiggle one finger.)
One named <u>Jill</u>.
(Wiggle the other finger.)
Fly away <u>Jack</u>.
(Whisk one hand behind your back.)
Fly away <u>Jill</u>.
(Whisk the other hand behind your back.)
Come back <u>Jack</u>.
(Have one finger come back.)
Come back <u>Jill</u>.
(Have the other finger come back.)

Special Considerations

Sincerely,

_____

SECONDARY
TARGET PATTERNS:
POSTVOCALIC
SYLLABIC /r/

POLAR BEAR, POLAR BEAR, WHAT DO YOU HEAR?

PATTERN

Postvocalic syllabic /ɾ/

TARGET PHONEME

Word-final vocalic /r/

TARGET WORDS

ear, bear, car, door

OPENING CENTER

GOAL

To introduce word-final vocalic /r/

MATERIALS

1. One set of alphabet letters (Appendix C)

2. Book titled *Polar Bear, Polar Bear, What Do You Hear?* (1991), by Bill Martin Jr.

> **Optional Materials**
>
> *Bucket of objects such as a bear, a doll with hair and an ear, a door on a car, a chair, the numeral 4, an animal with fur*

PROCEDURE

1. Introduce the letter *r* in the set of alphabet letters and demonstrate correct production of /r/. Sing the "Alphabet Song" (to the tune of "Twinkle, Twinkle, Little Star") and point to the letter *r* in the set of alphabet letters.

2. Have the children produce /r/ in isolation.

3. Introduce *Polar Bear, Polar Bear, What Do You Hear?* Point out the letter *r* in the title words *polar* and *bear*.

4. Read *Polar Bear, Polar Bear, What Do You Hear?* Model word-final vocalic /r/ in words as they occur in the story (e.g., *polar, bear, ear, hear*).

5. Sing the "Bear Song" and say the rhyme (play the game) "Red Rover, Red Rover."

"Bear Song"

One sunny day, when I was three,
I took a walk in forest green.
I saw a bear and froze with fear,
For he was standing oh so near.
I looked at him. He looked at me.
I saw how big one bear can be.
That big bear gave a mighty roar.
I didn't stay around for more.
I gave a shout and scared that bear.
I'm only three, but you beware—
that big bear took one look at me
and shimmied up the tallest tree.

"Red Rover, Red Rover"

(Have the children form two lines facing one another. The line is secured by children tightly holding hands. One side recites the verse requesting a child to come over to try to break through the line. If the child breaks through, he or she takes a person back to his or her side. If he or she doesn't break through, he or she stays with that line. The other side then gets a turn. Model word-final vocalic / r / in Rover *and* over.*)*

Red Rover, Red Rover,
send (child's name) right over.

LISTENING CENTER

GOAL

To provide clear auditory stimuli for word-final vocalic /r/

MATERIALS

1. One amplifier and one connector with headset per child

2. Listening list: *hear, tear, hair, chair, more, four, over, where, fur, near*

3. Illustrations of the four target words (pages 352–353; duplicate, cut out, and staple together)

4. Play dough

PROCEDURE

1. Instruct the children to wear their headsets and to listen. Speak into the amplifier and read the listening list to the children.

2. Introduce the four target words—*ear, bear, door, car*—to the children using the illustrations.

3. Instruct the children to continue wearing their headsets as you present a model of each target word. Have the children take turns repeating each word after it has been presented to each of them.

4. Tell the children to make happy faces out of the play dough and to add ears to the faces. Elicit /r/ in the word *ear*.

5. Have the children make roosters out of the play dough and have them crow "r-r-r-r-r."

Optional Activity

Using the play dough and the cookie cutters, help the children cut out cars, bears, or the letter r. Elicit vocalic /r/ from each child based on his or her skill level.

PRACTICE CENTER

GOAL

To facilitate production of word-final vocalic /r/

MATERIALS

1. One printed name card per child (see page 14)

2. Illustrations of the four target words (pages 352–353; duplicate, cut out, and staple together one set per child)

3. Colored markers

4. Each child's *Remediation Data Form* (Appendix B)

5. *Family Letter* (pages 356–357; duplicate one per child)

6. One speech folder per child

PROCEDURE

1. Have the children find their own name card. Once identified, instruct the children to finger-trace and say the letters in their names.

Optional Materials

Stickers ending in vocalic /r/ (e.g., bear or car stickers)

Optional Activity

Have the children choose a sticker to put on their folders. Then talk or ask questions about the sticker to elicit word-final vocalic /r/ productions (e.g., "You chose a _____ with brown _____." to elicit "bear" and "hair/fur").

2. Instruct the children to color the four target word illustrations—*ear, bear, car, door*—using the colored markers.

3. Have the children take turns naming the target word illustrations. The goal is to elicit word-final vocalic /r/.

4. Document the children's productions on their *Remediation Data Forms*.

5. Write notes related to each child's goal on his or her *Family Letter*.

ART CENTER

GOAL

To provide additional word-final vocalic /r/ production practice and to create visual aids for home activities

MATERIALS

1. *I Need an Ear to Hear!* (page 354; duplicate one per child)

2. One colored pencil per child

3. *Car Doors* (page 355; duplicate one per child)

4. Five different colored crayons per child

PROCEDURE

I Need an Ear to Hear!

1. Name the animals for the children and point out that their ears are missing.

2. Have the children use their colored pencil to draw ears on the animals. Model and elicit word-final vocalic /r/ in the words *ear, hear, polar,* and *bear* as the children draw.

3. Send the art page home in the child's speech folder.

Car Doors

1. Have the children use their crayons to color each car door a different color. Model and elicit word-final vocalic /r/ in the words *color, car,* and *door* as the children color.

2. Send the art page home in the child's speech folder.

HOME PRACTICE

GOAL

To provide home suggestions for what the children can do in the context of their everyday lives

MATERIALS

1. Each child's set of colored target word illustrations

2. Each child's completed art pages

3. Each child's speech folder

4. Each child's *Family Letter*

PROCEDURE

1. Collect the children's colored target word illustrations and completed art pages, and send them home in their speech folders.

2. Write any special instructions specific to a child on the *Family Letter*, on the target word illustrations, or on the art pages.

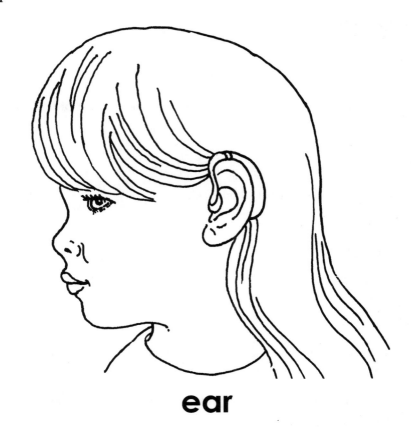

ear

bear

car

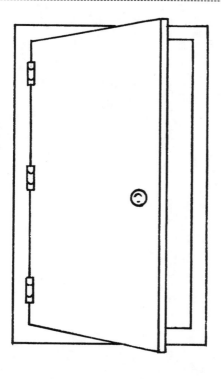

door

I Need an Ear to Hear!

Help the animals hear by drawing in their ears. Practice saying "hear" and "ear."

Color each car door a different color.
Practice saying "car" and "door."

Family Letter

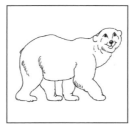

Date: _____

Dear Family,

The emphasis in this lesson is on producing *r* at the end of words. When making the *r* sound at the end of a word, the tongue is raised and drawn back from the upper teeth. The sides of the tongue may slightly touch the upper side gums. The teeth are slightly apart. The vocal cords vibrate.

The book for this lesson is *Polar Bear, Polar Bear, What Do You Hear?* by Eric Carle. While reading this story, the children will hear many final *r* sounds, such as in the phrase "*Polar Bear, Polar Bear*, what do you *hear*? I *hear* a lion roaring in my *ear*!" The book provides many opportunities to hear and say the *r* sound.

Listening List

Read this list to your child. Slightly emphasize the *r* sound at the end of each word.

hear	tear	hair	chair
more	four	over	where
fur	near		

Target Words

Using the pages in the speech folder, practice saying these words with your child. Follow the instructions provided at the end of this letter for any special considerations.

ear	door
bear	car

Suggested Home Activities

1. Read the story *Polar Bear, Polar Bear, What Do You Hear?* to your child. Slightly emphasize the *r* sound at the end of the words *bear* and *hear*.

2. Play road games with a car. Make car noises like "errr!"

3. Play Mr. Potato Head with your child. Have your child say *ear* as he or she puts each ear in place.

4. Sit quietly outside and talk about what you hear. Have your child repeat the phrase "I hear a _____."

5. Read *Goldilocks and the Three Bears* to your child. Slightly emphasize the word *bear* in the story.

6. Talk about the *I Need an Ear to Hear!* art page. Point to each ear your child has drawn and have him or her listen as you say *ear*.

7. Admire your child's coloring of the *Car Doors* art page. Ask your child to listen carefully and say the *r* sound in the words *car, door,* and *color*.

Songs and Games

The following song and game are being practiced in class. You can help your child use the *r* sound at the ends of words by having him or her listen as you slightly emphasize the *r* sound at the end of the underlined words.

"Bear Song"

One sunny day, when I was three,
I took a walk in forest green.
I saw a <u>bear</u> and froze with <u>fear</u>,
<u>For</u> he was standing oh so <u>near</u>.
I looked at him. He looked at me.
I saw how big one <u>bear</u> can be.
That big <u>bear</u> gave a mighty <u>roar</u>.
I didn't stay around for <u>more</u>.
I gave a shout and scared that <u>bear</u>.
I'm only three, but you <u>beware</u>—
that big <u>bear</u> took one look at me
and shimmied up the tallest tree.

"Red Rover, Red Rover"

(Have the children form two lines facing one another. The line is secured by children tightly holding hands. One side recites the verse requesting a child to come over and try to break through the line. If the child breaks through, he or she takes a person back to his or her side. If he or she doesn't break through, he or she stays with that line. The other side then gets a turn. Model the /r/ sound at the end of the words Rover *and* over.*)*

Red <u>Rover</u>, Red <u>Rover</u>,
send (child's name) right <u>over</u>.

Special Considerations

Sincerely,

_____

APPENDICES

IDEAS FOR HOME PRACTICE

Dear Family,

Each week, your child will be practicing a new sound or blend. The lessons used at school to learn the new sound or blend will use common storybooks that provide lots of opportunities to hear and say the targeted sound or blend. After each session at school, your child will be bringing home a speech folder. The speech folder will include illustrations of the target words being practiced at school, art pages or art activities completed at school, and a letter to you.

The letter will explain the focus of the lesson and how to say the sound or blend. It will also explain the book used in the lesson. Most books used are easily found at the public library. Other activities will be suggested in the letter to help your child use the new sounds or blends at home.

Please return the speech folder each day your child comes to school and check the speech folder when your child comes home. I may write special messages to you after each session. Please write back too. The following are ideas to make practice at home fun and rewarding for your child.

- Set aside a short, quiet time each day with your child for reading, singing, coloring, playing games, or doing activities. Incorporate the activities suggested in the letter during this time.

- Position yourself so that your child can see your face. Read the listening list to your child. Ask your child to listen carefully for the target sound or blend and to watch your face as you say each word.

- If you do not have the book used for the lesson, check it out at the public library if possible. Read the book with your child. As you read the book, pause after you say a word containing the target sound or blend. Pausing allows the child the opportunity to say the target word. You can also vary your intonation, rate of speaking, volume, and pitch for different characters in the book. The practice time together will help your child gain confidence speaking and making new speech sounds and blends.

- Review the lesson's song, rhyme, and/or fingerplay with your child. Use a slightly slower rate and carefully articulate the target sound or blend in words.

- Spend only five minutes daily with your child reviewing the four target words. Provide a correct model for the target sound or blend as your clinician has advised you in the *Family Letter*. Ask your child to repeat what you say.

- Display your child's art pages in your home. Praise your child's artwork and good effort in producing new speech sounds. Provide practice according to the instruction on the art page.

- Children will not always be able to say the target sound or blend in the practice words. Be specific with your praise. For example, if your child does not say the *l* sound correctly in words, you might say that you like the way he or she is learning to lift the tip of the tongue to the spot behind the top teeth.

- Try to incorporate speech sound work into your natural home environment as much as possible. For example, if the target sound for the lesson is the *w* sound, you could talk about the word *washing* while your child helps you add laundry to the washing machine. Do not be tempted, however, to correct your child's speech throughout the day or to interrupt when your child is speaking. Just provide enough home stimulation so that your child knows you care about his or her communication and the accomplishments that are happening.

- New skills are learned better in natural ways than through drill and practice. Help your child have fun with speech. Do the home activities suggested in the letter in enjoyable, interesting ways.

- If your child experiences difficulty with fluent speech (that is, stutters), I will speak with you about ideas for home practice.

- If your child shows hoarseness due to abuse of his or her voice, I will also meet with you to discuss ways to prevent vocal abuse.

If you need to reach me, I'm at _____.

Sincerely,

_____

REMEDIATION DATA FORM

Name: _____

Speech-Language Pathologist: _____

DATE	TARGET	LESSON	RESULTS
			Day 1—Target: Day 2—Target: Observation:
			Day 1—Target: Day 2—Target: Observation:
			Day 1—Target: Day 2—Target: Observation:
			Day 1—Target: Day 2—Target: Observation:
			Day 1—Target: Day 2—Target: Observation:
			Day 1—Target: Day 2—Target: Observation:

ILLUSTRATED ALPHABET

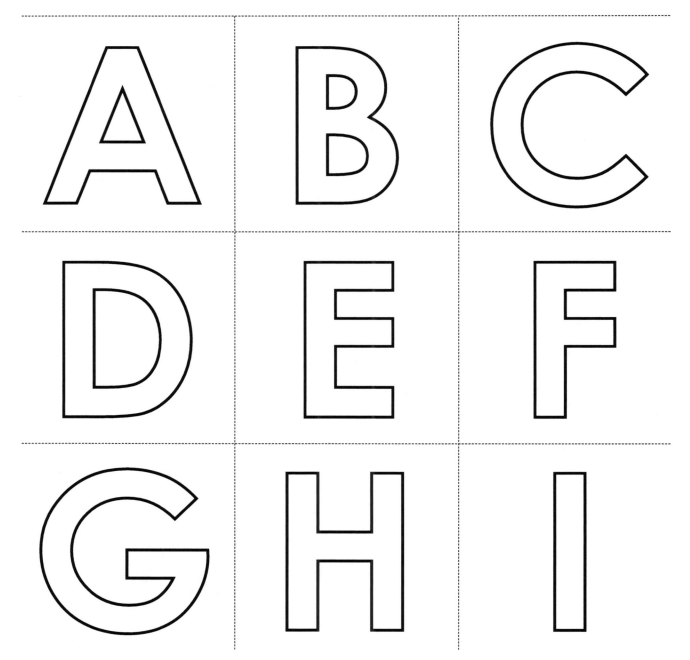

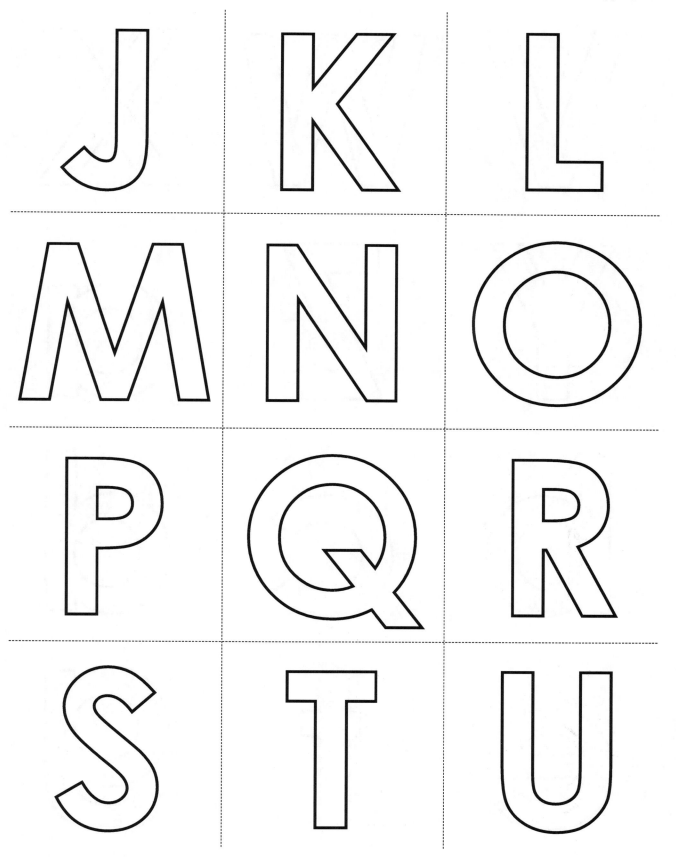

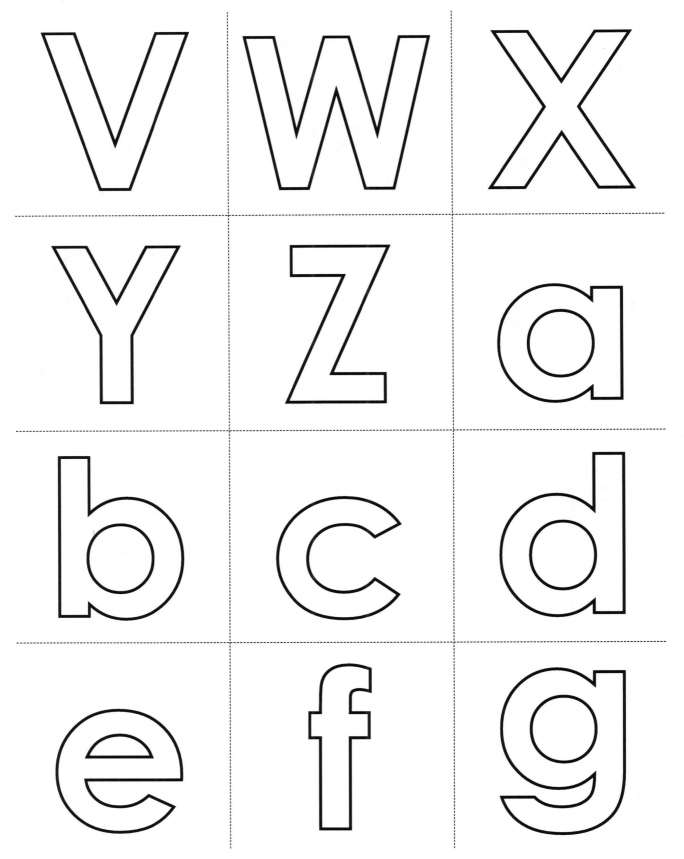

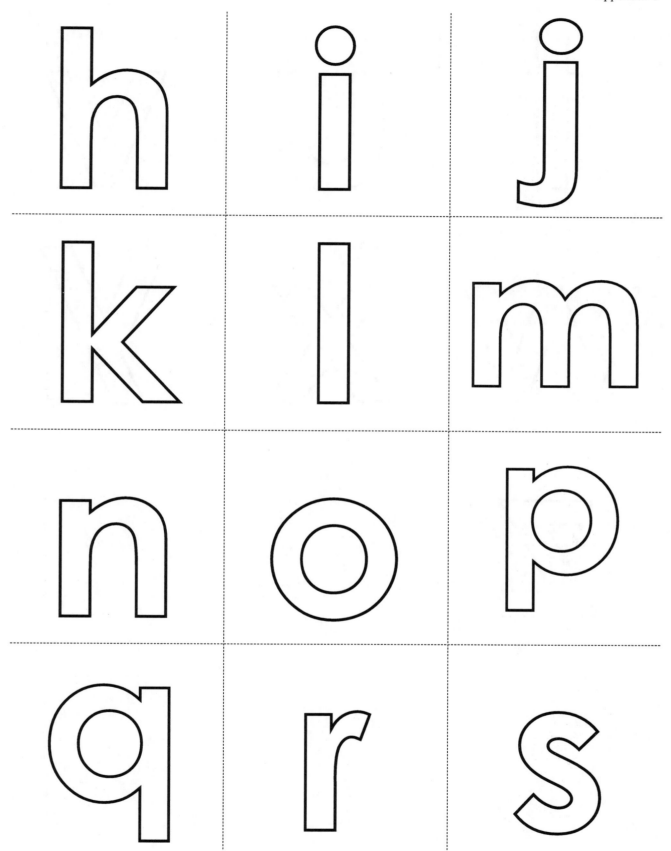

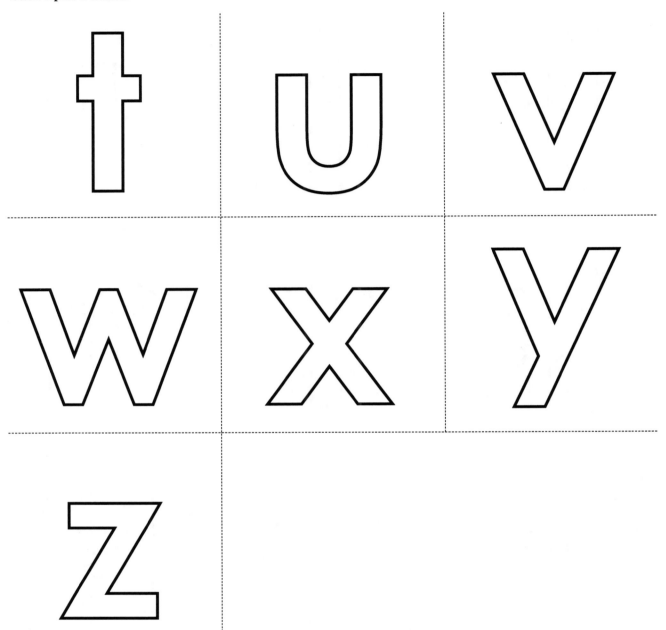

PHONOLOGICAL CYCLES SAMPLES

The following are examples of cycles for three children. Note that primary target pattern phonemes are addressed first and then later cycles address secondary target patterns. For these children, cycles include early developing patterns that rarely need targeting. Order of presentation was based on each child's individual needs and also considered group needs.

SAMPLE 1

Cycle 1

Syllableness
Word-initial /w/
Word-initial /m/
Word-initial /p/
Word-final /t/
Word-final /k/
Word-initial /h/
Word-initial /sp/
Word-final /ps/
Word-initial /l/
Word-initial /st/

Cycle 2

Word-initial /t/
Word-initial /l/
Word-final /ts/
Word-final /k/
Word-initial /k/
Word-initial /r/
Word-initial /g/

Cycle 3

Word-final /f/
Word-initial /f/
Word-final /r/
Word-initial /tʃ/
Word-final /ʃ/

Cycle 4

Word-initial /dʒ/
Word-initial /f/

SAMPLE 2

Cycle 1

Word-final /t/
Word-final /k/
Word-final /ps/
Word-initial /sp/
Word-initial /st/
Word-initial /sn/
Word-initial /sm/
Word-initial /l/

Cycle 2

Word-final /ts/
Word-final /k/
Word-initial /k/
Word-initial /l/
Word-initial /r/

Cycle 3

Word-final /r/
Word-initial /g/
Word-final /ʃ/
Word-final /f/
Word-initial /f/
Word-initial /ʃ/

Cycle 4

Word-initial /f/
Word-initial /tʃ/
Word-initial /dʒ/

SAMPLE 3

Cycle 1

Word-initial /sp/
Word-initial /st/
Word-initial /sn/
Word-initial /sm/
Word-final /k/
Word-initial /l/

Cycle 2

Word-final /k/
Word-initial /k/
Word-initial /l/
Word-initial /r/

Cycle 3

Word-initial /g/
Word-final /ʃ/
Word-final /f/
Word-initial /f/
Word-final /r/
Word-initial /ʃ/
Word-initial /tʃ/

SPEECH ONLY SERVICE DATA

Minneapolis Public Schools
Early Childhood Special Education
Speech and Language Services

Site

St. Helena School

Students Served

This program serves preschool children between the ages of three and five who have severe or profound communication disorders but no other measured cognitive, motor, or other developmental delays. The majority of these children are highly unintelligible. These children tend to have a phonological disorder, which may be coupled with other communication disorders (e.g., phonology and language, phonology and fluency).

Speech-Language Service

Children receive a minimum of 120 minutes of direct speech-language services per week, in two 60-minute sessions. Children with the most severe communication disorders have the option of receiving four 60-minute sessions per week. Speech and language services are delivered to groups of three to six children. As described in *Once Upon a Sound,* family involvement is an important part of every child's educational program.

Service Data

Total IEPs	Exited from Service at End of Year	Return for Service Next Year as 4 yr. olds	Moved out of District	Continued IEPs for Communication in Kindergarten
1997–98 46	17 (37%)	13 (28%)	6 (13%)	10 (22%)
1996–97 54	17 (31%)	10 (19%)	11 (20%)	16 (30%)
1995–96 54	22 (41%)	12 (22%)	9 (17%)	11 (20%)
1994–95 51	20 (39%)	11 (22%)	6 (12%)	15 (29%)
1993–94 50	20 (40%)	6 (12%)	10 (20%)	14 (28%)

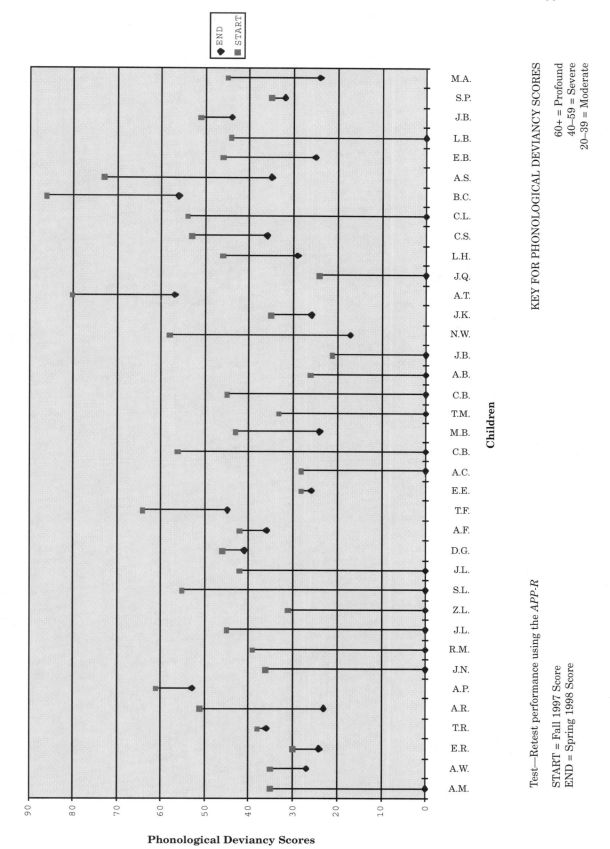

1997–98 Progress Report of Individual Students in ECSE Program

Phonological Deviancy Scores

Children

KEY FOR PHONOLOGICAL DEVIANCY SCORES

60+ = Profound
40–59 = Severe
20–39 = Moderate

Test—Retest performance using the *APP-R*

START = Fall 1997 Score
END = Spring 1998 Score

One Student's Progress in Phonological Development*

Student Name: _____   Date: _____

CA: 3-4	*CA: 3-10*	*CA: 4-4*	*CA: 4-10*
Date: _10-93_	**Date:** _4-94_	**Date:** _10-94_	**Date:** _4-95_

Syllable Reduction: _16_	Syllable Reduction: _0_	Syllable Reduction: _0_	Syllable Reduction: _0_
Prevocalic Singletons: _25_	Prevocalic Singletons: _20_	Prevocalic Singletons: _0_	Prevocalic Singletons: _0_
Postvocalic Singletons: _100_	Postvocalic Singletons: _45_	Postvocalic Singletons: _3_	Postvocalic Singletons: _0_
Consonant Sequences: _100_	Consonant Sequences: _68_	Consonant Sequences: _10_	Consonant Sequences: _3_
Stridents: _93_	Stridents: _60_	Stridents: _2_	Stridents: _0_
Velars: _55_	Velars: _45_	Velars: _9_	Velars: _0_
Liquid /l/ _100_	Liquid /l/ _100_	Liquid /l/ _64_	Liquid /l/ _0_
Liquid /r/ _48_	Liquid /r/ _48_	Liquid /r/ _5_	Liquid /r/ _10_
Nasals: _68_	Nasals: _58_	Nasals: _0_	Nasals: _0_
Glides: _60_	Glides: _20_	Glides: _20_	Glides: _0_
Backing: _20_	Backing: _20_	Backing: _30_	Backing: _0_
Average of Phonological Processes: _68_	Average of Phonological Processes: _46_	Average of Phonological Processes: _11_	Average of Phonological Processes: _1_
Phonological Deviancy Score: _68_	Phonological Deviancy Score: _46_	Phonological Deviancy Score: _—_	Phonological Deviancy Score: _____
Severity Interval: _____	Severity Interval: _____	Severity Interval: _____	Severity Interval: _____
Profound	*Severe*	*This client is not a candidate for a phonological approach.*	*This client is no longer a candidate for a phonological approach.*

* *As measured by the*
  Assessment of Phonological Processes—R

BIBLIOGRAPHY

Brown Bear, Brown Bear, What Do You See? (1983), by Bill Martin Jr., pictures
   by Eric Carle
   New York: Holt

Caps for Sale (1968), by Esphyr Slobodkina
   New York: Scholastic

Chicka Chicka Boom Boom (1989), by Bill Martin Jr. and John Archambault,
   illustrated by Lois Ehlert
   New York: Simon and Schuster

Cookie's Week (1997), by Cindy Ward, illustrated by Tomie DePaola
   New York: Putnam

Draw Me a Star (1992), by Eric Carle
   New York: Philomel Books

Each Peach Pear Plum (1978), by Janet and Allan Ahlberg
   New York: Puffin Books

Five Little Ducks (1989), by Raffi, illustrated by José Aruego and Ariane Dewey
   New York: Crown

Frosty the Snow Man (1950), by Annie North Bedford
   Racine, WI: Western Publishing

The Gingerbread Man (1985), illustrated by Karen Lee Schmidt
   New York: Scholastic

Goodnight Moon (1975), by Margaret Wise Brown, pictures by Clement Hurd
   New York: HarperTrophy

Hop on Pop (1991), by Dr. Seuss
   New York: Random House

How Do You Say It Today, Jesse Bear? (1994), by Nancy White Carlstrom
   New York: Scholastic

I Am King (1994), by Mary Packard, illustrated by Leonid Gore
   Chicago: Childrens Press

I Went Walking (1990), by Sue Williams, illustrated by Julie Vivas
San Diego, CA: Gulliver Books

It Looked Like Spilt Milk (1947), by Charles G. Shaw
New York: Harper and Row

Jump, Frog, Jump! (1995), by Robert Kalan, pictures by Byron Barton
New York: Marrow

Marvin K. Mooney, Will You Please Go Now! (1972), by Dr. Seuss
New York: Random House

Moo Moo, Brown Cow (1992), by Jakki Wood, illustrated by Rog Bonner
San Diego, CA: Harcourt Brace

Polar Bear, Polar Bear, What Do You Hear? (1991), by Bill Martin Jr.,
pictures by Eric Carle
New York: Holt

Quick as a Cricket (1982), by Audrey Wood
New York: Scholastic

Red Is Best (1992), by Kathy Stinson, illustrated by Robin Baird Lewis
Buffalo, NY: Firefly Books

Shake My Sillies Out (1987), by Raffi, illustrated by David Allender
New York: Crown

Sheep in a Shop (1991), by Nancy Shaw, illustrated by Margot Apple
Boston: Houghton Mifflin

The Snowy Day (1962), by Ezra Jack Keats
New York: Viking Press

Teddy Bear, Teddy Bear (1993), illustrated by Michael Hague
New York: Morrow

The Three Little Pigs (1973), by Elizabeth Ross
Racine, WI: Western Publishing

Wheels on the Bus (1988), by Raffi, illustrated by Sylvie Kantorovitz Wickstrom
New York: Crown

Where's the Fish? (1977), by Taro Gomi
New York: Morrow

Where's Spot? (1980), by Eric Hill
New York: Putnam

REFERENCES

Adams, M. (1990). *Beginning to read.* Cambridge, MA: Massachusetts Institute of Technology Press.

Anderson, P., and Graham, S. (1994). Issues in second-language phonological acquisition among children and adults. *Topics in Language Disorders, 14*(2), 84–100.

Bird, J., Bishop, D.V.M., and Freeman, N.H. (1995). Phonological awareness and literacy development in children with expressive phonological impairments. *Journal of Speech and Hearing Research, 38,* 446–462.

Blachman, B. (1984). Language analysis skills and early reading acquisition. In G. Wallach and K. Butler (Eds.), *Language learning disabilities in school-age children* (pp. 271–287). Baltimore, MD: Williams and Wilkins.

Bonderman, I., and Montgomery, J. (1986). *A preschool program for severe phonological disorders* [booklet]. Fountain Valley, CA: Fountain Valley School District.

Bradley L., and Bryant, P. (1983). Categorizing sounds and learning to read: A causal connection. *Nature, 301,* 419–421.

Broen, P., Doyle, S., and Bacon, C. (1993). The velopharyngeally inadequate child: Phonologic change with intervention. *Cleft Palate-Craniofacial Journal, 30,* 500–507.

Catts, H. (1991). Facilitating phonological awareness: The role of speech-language pathologists. *Language, Speech, and Hearing Services in Schools, 22,* 196–204.

Catts, H. (1993). The relationship between speech-language impairments and reading disabilities. *Journal of Speech and Hearing Research, 36,* 948–958.

Cirrin, F. (1994). Assessing language in the classroom and the curriculum. In J.B. Tomblin, H.L. Morris, and D.C. Sprietersbach (Eds.), *Diagnosis in speech-language pathology* (pp. 135–164). San Diego, CA: Singular.

Clarke-Klein, S.M. (1994). Expressive phonological deficiencies: Impact on spelling development. *Topics in Language Disorders, 14*(2) 40–55.

Compton, A. (1970). Generative studies of children's phonological disorders. *Journal of Speech and Hearing Disorders, 35,* 315–339.

Gierut, J.A. (1998). Treatment efficacy: Functional phonological disorders in children. *Journal of Speech and Hearing Research, 41,* S85–S100.

Grunwell, P. (1985). *Phonological assessment of child speech.* Windsor, England: NFER-Nelson.

Hodson, B. (1985). *Computer analysis of phonological processes.* Stonington, IL: PhonoComp.

Hodson, B. (1986). *The assessment of phonological processes–revised.* San Antonio, TX: Pro-Ed.

Hodson, B. (1992). *Computer analysis of phonological deviations.* Stonington, IL: PhonoComp.

Hodson, B. (1994). Helping individuals become intelligible, literate, and articulate: The role of phonology. *Topics in Language Disorders, 14*(2), 1–16.

Hodson, B. (1998, February). *Enhancing phonological, metaphonological, and emergent literacy skills.* Paper presented at the Illinois Speech-Language-Hearing Association annual convention, Arlington Heights, IL.

Hodson, B. (1997). Disordered phonologies: What have we learned about assessment and treatment? In B.W. Hodson and M.L. Edwards (Eds.) *Perspectives in applied phonology* (pp. 197–224). Gaithersburg, MD: Aspen.

Hodson, B., and Paden, E. (1991). *Targeting intelligible speech: A phonological approach to remediation.* San Antonio, TX: Pro-Ed.

Hoffman, P. (1992). Synergistic development of phonetic skill. *Language, Speech, and Hearing Services in Schools, 23,* 254–260.

Jenkins, R., and Bowen, L. (1994). Facilitating development of preliterate children's phonological abilities. *Topics in Language Disorders, 14*(2), 26–39.

Johnson, K., and Heinze, B. (1994). *The fluency companion.* East Moline, IL: LinguiSystems.

Kaderavek, J., and Sulzby, E. (1998). Parent-child joint book reading: An observational protocol for young children. *American Journal of Speech-Language Pathology, 7*(1), 33–47.

Kalan, R. (1995). *Jump, frog, jump!* New York: Morrow.

Kamhi, A. (1992). The need for a broad-based model of phonological disorders. *Language, Speech, and Hearing Services in Schools, 23,* 261–268.

Kaufman, N. (1997). *Evaluation and treatment of children with developmental apraxia of speech.* Gaylord, MI: Northern Speech Services.

Kelman, M., and Edwards, M. (1994). *Phonogroup.* Eau Claire, WI: Thinking Publications.

Kent, R. (1982). Contextual facilitation of correct sound production. *Language, Speech, and Hearing Services in Schools, 13,* 66–76.

Khan, L., and Lewis, N. (1986). *Khan-Lewis phonological analysis.* Circle Pines, MN: American Guidance Service.

Klein, E. (1996). Phonological/traditional approaches to articulation therapy: A retrospective group comparison. *Language, Speech, and Hearing Services in Schools, 27,* 314–322.

McFadden, T. (1998). Sounds and stories: Teaching phonemic awareness in interactions around text. *American Journal of Speech-Language Pathology, 7*(2), 5–13.

Montgomery, J. (1992, February). Books, books, books. *Clinically Speaking, 9*(1), 1–2. (Available from the Western Hills Area Education Agency, Speech-Language Services, 1520 Morningside Avenue, Sioux City, IA 51106)

Montgomery, J., and Bonderman, I. (1989). Serving preschool children with severe phonological disorders. *Language, Speech, and Hearing Services in Schools, 20,* 76–84.

Norris, J., and Hoffman, P. (1993). *Whole language intervention for school-age children.* San Diego, CA: Singular.

Oller, D. (1973). Regularities in abnormal child phonology. *Journal of Speech and Hearing Disorders, 38,* 36–47.

Ruscello, D.M. (1991). School-aged children with phonologic disorders: Coexistence with other speech-language disorders. *Journal of Speech and Hearing Research, 34,* 236–242.

Shriberg, L., and Kwiatkowski, J. (1980). *Natural process analysis.* New York: Wiley.

Shelton, R.L., Johnson, A.E., and Arndt, W.B. (1972). Monitoring and reinforcement by parents as a means of automating articulatory responses. *Perceptual and Motor Skills, 35,* 759–767.

Smith-Kiewel, L., and Claeys, T. (1997, April) *A preschool program for children with severe communication disorders.* Paper presented at the Minnesota Speech-Language-Hearing Association annual convention, Minneapolis, MN.

Stackhouse, J. (1997). Phonological awareness: Connecting speech and literacy problems. In B.W. Hodson and M.L. Edwards (Eds.), *Perspective in applied phonology* (pp. 157–196). Gaithersburg, MD: Aspen.

Stackhouse, J. (1992). Developmental verbal dyspraxia: A longitudinal case study. In R. Campbell (Ed.), *Mental lives; case studies in cognition* (pp. 84–98). Oxford, UK: Basil Blackwell.

Stone, J. (1992). *The animated alphabet.* La Mesa, CA: J. Stone Creations.

van Kleeck, A. (1993, April). *Music and literature as contexts for preschool language intervention.* Paper presented at the Minnesota Speech-Language Hearing-Association annual convention, Minneapolis, MN.